Wayne Short

LUKE SHORT

FRONTIER GAMBLER

LUKE SHORT

A BIOGRAPHY

by WAYNE SHORT

DEVIL'S THUMB PRESS

Cover Photo from Short Collection

Copyright 1996© Wayne Short

OTHER BOOKS by WAYNE SHORT:
THE CHEECHAKOES
THIS RAW LAND
ALBIE, & BILLY, THE SKYPILOT

ISBN: 0-9644980-7-3

Devil's Thumb Press, Box 688, Tombstone, AZ 85638

DEDICATION

This book is dedicated to my great-grandparents, Josiah Washington Short (1812-1890) and Hettie Brumley Short (1826-1908).

And especially for my late father, Walter Lucian Short, who continued pioneering in Alaska. Dad showed me by example that a person could reject regimentation, and be successful in his own unique way.

ACKNOWLEDGMENT

My thanks to my aunt, Ruth Short Irvin, and Margaret, who encouraged me to begin this book, sent me material and old photographs . . . and corrected me when I went astray.

Also to Uncle Henry Short for his stories and family material.

Wayne Short

AUTHOR'S NOTE

In 1960, I received a letter from Frederick D. Glidden, a noted author, writing under the pen name of Luke Short. He told me how he came to use my great-uncle's name, Luke Short, as a pseudonym. It was picked by his New York literary agent, Margarite Harper, back in the 1930's when she first sold a western short story for him. By the time Mr. Glidden hit the best selling status and movie sales, he said he was comfortable having Luke Short on his book covers.

In his letter to me, Mr. Glidden wrote that one of his fellow writers, William R. Cox, was doing research for a biography of my great-uncle Luke, but was having trouble obtaining information on his early life. He asked if I could assist Mr. Cox, and I furnished enough family material to Mr. Cox that he could complete *Luke Short, and His Era.*

As the years went by and I sold short stories and books, I decided some day I would do a full biography of my famous great-uncle.

This book is a result of years of drawing the old family stories out of my late father, Walter L. Short. These stories, with the many bits and pieces published of Luke Short in books, magazines, newspapers of the days and government records make a more complete history of his life.

Since so much of the material came from my father and family, I have used end notes only when I thought they were necessary. I have also recreated dialogue in places in the interest of the story, but I believe this is as close to the original as is possible after more than a hundred years.

Wayne Short
Tombstone, Arizona

INTRODUCTION

Luke Short, who counted among his friends such notables as Bat Masterson, Wyatt Earp, Doc Holliday, William Harris, Dick Clark, Charlie and Joe Bassett, and many other personalities of the Old West, was no less a noteworthy figure in his own right. Part of the reason for his lack of recognition is that little was known of his early life, and the fact he died at a comparatively young age, while both Masterson and Earp lived well into this century, and had much written about them. But Luke Short made a place for himself as an honest, high rolling gambler in the cowtowns and mining camps in Kansas, Nebraska, Colorado, and Arizona. His loyalty to his friends was absolute, and they dropped whatever they were doing and came from all over the West to aid him during the Dodge City Saloon War of 1883.

Later, he returned to Texas, from whence he had come, and successfully co-owned and operated the elegant and popular White Elephant Saloon, Restaurant, and Gambling Hall in Fort Worth.

Luke's parents and grandparents had been pioneers and it was in their blood to press westward, seeking new lands and opportunities. Though there were a multitude of hardships along the way; they gambled on the possibility they would survive and prosper, in a dangerous and fast growing America. Luke's destiny, by a stroke of fate, was to press farther west and develop his own life-style in a vastly different way than his forbears. This life-style was in keeping with the opportunities he encountered at a young and impressionable age.

This is the story of his adventurous life.

CHAPTER ONE

Luke Short's grandfather, Josiah Short, had immigrated to Virginia from England sometime in the late 1790's. Soon he moved on to North Carolina where he married and started a family. Later, he moved his family to Tennessee, cleared land, and farmed. In 1812, Luke's father was born, and was named Josiah Washington Short. Young Josiah never cared for his long name, and was soon called, simply, Wash.

Wash grew up in Tennessee, and worked on his father's farm. In his late twenties, he left home and went to visit his former neighbors who had moved to Mississippi. Their name was Brumley. John Brumley had a large plantation and raised fine thoroughbred race horses. He also had a lovely daughter named Hettie.

Her family was Scotch-Irish, and well to do. Wash worked for John Brumley on his plantation and courted Hettie. It was a long wait, for Wash was fourteen years older than Hettie, and Hettie's parents insisted she be twenty before she was married.

Wash Short and Hettie Brumley were finally married in early 1846. Shortly afterward they moved farther west into Arkansas, where they settled on the banks of the Ouachita River, in Polk County. There they farmed, and began their own family. In 1847 their first child was born, a daughter who was named, Martha. Next came John Pleasant, named for

Hettie's father. In 1852 Josiah Washington Jr. was born. Wash probably remembered how he disliked his own long name, and the little boy was simply called, Joe. Another boy, Young, was born in 1852, followed by Luke in 1854. Mary Catherine came two years later, then Henry in 1859.[1]

Sometime in the 1850's, one of Wash's sisters and her husband moved to Arkansas and settled nearby. They brought Wash's elderly father with them. The old Englishman was widowed, and his eyes and hearing were failing him.

The Shorts had good years there on the Ouachita River, but shortly after Henry was born, they began to think of moving to Texas. There were several reasons for this. First, their good farming land along the river was limited, for most of the property was in rolling hills. The second reason was that Hettie's parents had sold their plantation in Mississippi, and moved to northern Texas along the Red River, in Montague County. Hettie's father, John, kept writing and encouraging Wash and Hettie, to sell out and move near him, citing the good land that could be bought for a nominal price. Texas had kept control of her public lands, and a percentage of it was designated as School Lands. When this land was sold to settlers, the monies were put into a fund to build and operate public schools.

Another reason Wash and Hettie were serious about leaving Arkansas: war. For years there had been friction between the Free and the Slave States. They feared if war broke out, they might be too near an area where bitter violence might jeopardise them and their children. Parts of Kansas and Missouri were already bitterly divided. At least the move to Texas would put them back among the solid South.

After making their decision to leave, Wash found a buyer and sold the farm. The only problem bothering them was the move through country often raided by Comanche and Kiowa Indians.

This problem was soon settled when John Brumley sent three of Hettie's grown brothers to help with the move and to protect them from Indians.

CHAPTER TWO

They set out early one morning, their possessions stowed in two large covered wagons each pulled by three spans of oxen. Wash drove one wagon with Hettie, the girls, and baby Henry. Hettie's brother, John, drove the other wagon, with Luke as his companion. The three oldest Short boys, John, Joe, and Young, rode and drove the rest of the horses and three milk cows. Hettie's other two brothers, Will and Luke Brumley, were well-armed and led the little caravan as it rolled south.

Will, the eldest of the three Brumley brothers was a sheriff in Texas, and a seasoned Indian fighter. He had decided on the route through southern Arkansas, crossing the Red River near what is now New Boston, then turning west and taking the wagon road that paralleled the Red River through Bowie, Red River, Lamar, Fannin, Grayson and Cooke Counties.

Though their move was little more that 250 miles, Hettie was glad when it was over. They had run into no hostile Indians, and lost no stock. All the children were healthy, except for Luke, now five years old. Luke's health had always been fragile, and now he was plagued with a fever. He lay on a pallet behind Hettie's seat in the wagon, and Martha tended him.

Hettie breathed a sigh of relief when at last the wagons pulled up in front of her parents' large, comfortable home, and they were all reunited. They got Luke inside and put him to bed. Her mother soon had the fever broken and he was on the mend.

Hettie was thrilled to meet her siblings, the younger ones whom she had not seen before. Some of her own children were about the same ages of her little brothers and sister. They settled in with the Brumleys, and soon Wash bought fertile school land on Elm Fork Creek from the state.

John Brumley and Wash, though father and son-in-law, were actually close in age in that year of 1859. Wash was forty-six, and John Brumley was only eight years his senior. The Brumley men jumped in and helped Wash and his boys build a log house for his family. It was really two log cabins connected by a covered dogtrot, much like the one left in Arkansas. Wash and Hettie, together with the girls and baby Henry slept in one side, and the older boys slept in the other.

The Brumley's had experienced raids by both Comanches and Kiowas in the past, so they made rifle slots into the two buildings which could be opened in almost every direction. The gun ports could be plugged in normal times, but quickly opened to give a good view of the outbuildings and corrals where they would be built. John Brumley said the Texas Rangers had recently tracked down and killed a bunch of raiding Kiowas, but that the situation could change. Better keep you eyes peeled, John said, and keep the rifles loaded and ready. John also warned them to keep a sharp eye on their blooded horses. He said the beautiful horses drew Indians like bears to a honey tree.

The log houses had been built on a small rise, that gave a good view of anyone approaching. Nearby was a good natural spring with cold, clear water. Wash and the boys built a log spring house that covered the spring, and Hettie kept fresh milk and buttermilk and butter there in the coolness. They also built a smokehouse and a barn and corrals. Then Wash and his three older boys went to work clearing the land with their oxen, getting it ready for crops.

The next spring they planted corn and wheat and cotton, and some sugar cane and sorghum. The nearest settlement was Saint Jo, and it was here they had to travel for staples and farming supplies. John Brumley had given his son-in-law enough chickens and hogs and cattle to feed them and get their own animals started, and it wasn't long before they were fairly self-sufficient. By the fall after the first planting, they were taking wheat and corn to Saint Jo to the mill and returning with flour and cornmeal. What they didn't require for their own use, they sold, and used the money to buy staples. They began to make a little money from their cotton, and as time went on, planted more. From the sorghum they made molasses. Soon they had plenty of chickens and eggs, and began to butcher hogs and make sausage and sugar cured bacon and hams which they smoked in their smokehouse.

Somewhere around this time, Grandpap Short arrived from Arkansas to live with them. Very likely he came with other settlers who were moving to the Red River Country. He bunked with the older boys in their log cabin.

Trousers were expensive in those days, and the little boys simply wore long homespun shirts until they were about six years of age. The shirts were of cotton in the summer, and wool in the winter. Luke received his first pair of big boy overalls there in Montague County, in 1860, and was proud to finally get them. Many years later, Joe Short would recall that after supper there was a rule that all the children must fill their shoes with seeds they picked from cotton boles. Their mother would then card and spin the cotton. Hettie was also recognized for her nursing skills in the area. She delivered babies far and wide, riding her pet horse, Billy, or traveling many miles at night in a wagon to treat the sick or wounded.

She learned her skills from her mother, from experience,

and from reading medical books. After each of her own children were born, she was up and going about her work within two hours. She never had patience with women who stayed in their beds after the birth of their babies. This later included her own daughters and daughter-in-laws.

It is hard to imagine a woman raising seven children, doing the house work, helping with the making of sausage and curing of hams, churning milk into butter, sewing all the clothing, and being ready to help fight Indians when they came raiding.

These were good times for the family, even though all of them had to work hard, even the children when they were old enough to help. They had the large Brumley family near, and had made other friends, though these neighbors were some distance away. The Indians had not bothered them, and the only problem on the horizon, was the talk of war. In the election of 1860, Abraham Lincoln had won the presidency. The next year South Carolina, Georgia, Florida, Alabama, Mississippi, Louisiana, and Texas seceded from the union.

Jefferson Davis had been wrestling with the problem of secession, but hoped to avoid war with the northern states. After Lincoln decided to try and hold on to the two southern fortresses, Fort Pickens in Florida, and Fort Sumter in South Carolina, war was inevitable. When the north tried to reinforce these forts, the South fired on Fort Sumter, and the war was joined. Virginia, North Carolina, Tennessee, and Arkansas soon joined the Confedercy. Slave states of Missouri, Kentucky, West Virgina, and Maryland were in sympathy with the South, but elected not to secede.

Though Texas was far away from the fighting, the war soon enveloped them all. By the spring of 1862, William, Luke, and John Brumley, Jr. had joined the Confederate Army, and went east to fight. The Texans, with a fierceness that surprised no one, left their businesses, farms, ranches, and families to fight, much as they had before when they rallied to fight Santa Ana and Mexico. Consequently, most of the Texas Rangers were also drawn away.

The Comanches and Kiowas were quick to perceive this, and were soon raiding the frontier settlements, killing and torturing victims, kidnapping children and young women, and running off stock.

It was to be a tough time for the Shorts. All of the boys were good shots, as was their mother, Hettie, but they were spread thin trying to work the farm land and protect their home at the same time. They soon developed a system: Wash and the three older boys worked the fields and made the trips to Saint Jo to pick up supplies, while Luke and his mother defended the homestead. Wash and his sons all carried single shot rifles, and had a revolver or two. With their fire power, they could, by firing in relays, hold off a fair sized bunch of Indians. The houses were solidly built of heavy logs, the cracks chinked with moss and clay mud; the doors were of thick oak, with heavy forged hinges, and two thick oak beams barred them on the inside from attack. In the event a battering ram or a horse was backed into them, a slot had been cut into the center of the door that could be fired through. Luke and his mother had two old muzzleloading, smoothbore rifles, and a newer 1852 short barreled Sharps of .52 caliber. The Sharps was a percussion rifle, and, though it was also single shot, could be reloaded quickly. It was Luke's favorite. They also had a shotgun. Martha was the chief reloader, and was able to keep a loaded rifle in Luke's or her mother's hands if it was needed.

They had orders to double bar the doors and be quiet, when Indians raided them at night. If the Indians took stock, well, it couldn't be helped. The main thing was to keep anyone from being killed or taken prisoner.

In 1862 Luke was only eight years old, yet he was able to

help hold off Comanche and Kiowa war parties from the little fort there on Elm Fork. The log barns and the large smokehouse were also fitted with heavy doors that could be locked, and if war parties were thought to be in the area, their prize horses were locked in at dark.

Sometimes raiding Indians would ride up to the houses at night when Wash and the older boys were gone, and try to peer between the logs, where caulking might have fallen out, to see if there were men inside. The Short's dogs always gave the Indians away, and as soon as the defenders knew there were Indians outside, they extinguished the candles and lamps and stayed quiet. On these occasions, they tried to not let Grandpap know that Indians were outside, for on one occasion, he had run outside with the shotgun before they had the door barred, and almost run into a Comanche. "Avast, yon grand rascal!" the old Englishman cried, and fired his shotgun. His eyesight was so bad, however, he had aimed for a stump instead of the startled Comanche, who promptly took off. The family soon learned it was better to let the Indians simply ride away when they saw they could not easily break in.

Most Indians were really guerilla fighters, with hit and run tactics; they were brave, especially when attacked and their women and children were in danger. They could be suicidal in this kind of bravery, but their main style of fighting was to raid and to kill with the least amount of loss to themselves. When they had overwhelming superiority, they would go for the kill, but let a determined opponent with a rifle kill several of them, they might soon lose heart and leave.

On one occasion while Wash and the older boys were away, Hettie and the others were raided by a band of Kiowas. One of the family, always on watch, spotted them coming, and Luke and his mother were able to lock all of the blooded horses into the barn and smokehouse before the Indians got there. When two Indians tried to force the door of the barn open, Luke killed one and wounded the other with a leg shot. The remaining Indians quickly got out of sight behind the barn, but Hettie caught one brave peeking around the side, and either hit him or sent splinters into his face with a shot. The Indians decided it was not worth it, and soon took off with the dead man and their wounded, but before they left, they shot all the hogs in the pen full of arrows.

When Wash and the other boys got back, they found the whole family killing and butchering the squealing hogs. The family just couldn't afford to waste the meat, so they cut up the hogs, and made sausage, and put the bacons and hams into crocks for sugar and salt curing.

They lost cattle and horses on these raids, but there was little they could do about it. They were thankful that none of the family had been killed. Their neighbors weren't so lucky. The father and mother were killed in one family, and their bodies mutilated in front of their children. Then the children were taken by the Indians. Another family, who lived not far from the Shorts, were the Boxes. In 1866, James Box was killed by Kiowas as he and his family were driving home in a wagon. The Indians scalped and mutilated him in front of his family, and cut out his heart. They took Mrs. Box, her baby, and three daughters captive. The girls' names were Margaret, about seventeen, Josephine, thirteen, and Ida, seven. Margaret kept running back to her father's body, and Mrs. Box could see the Indians were about ready to kill her, too, so she ordered Margaret to go peaceably with them.[1]

Mrs. Mary Box had just given birth to her baby a few weeks before and when the baby kept crying, the Kiowas finally took it from her, threw it upon the ground, and killed it with rocks. Not long thereafter the Indians separated, sending Mrs. Box and Josephine with one band, Margaret and Ida with others. When they arrived at their camp, Ida kept running around crying out for her sisters and mother. Finally, the Kiowa squaws got tired of it and held her feet in the coals of the fire so that she couldn't run and bother them.

In the Indian camp where Josephine was held, one of her chores was to gather firewood with the other Indian girls. One day when they were out gathering wood, one of the Indian girls began picking on her, and Josephine gave her a good whipping. Josephine said after this the Kiowas treated her much better. Apparently they respected her for her courage.

After about eighteen months, the Texas government was able to buy Mrs. Box and her daughters back from Santanta, the infamous Kiowa chief.

Another girl captive was repeatedly burned on the nose by a firebrand. By the time the poor thing was rescued, there was nothing left of the nose—just a hole where the nose had been. These rescued or ransomed captives hardly ever recovered mentally from their treatment. Women and girl captives were repeatedly raped, and any man unlucky enough to be taken captive, could count on a slow, and painful torture of the worst kind by the Comanches and Kiowas. To be a Texan between the 1830's and the early 1870's was to be an Indian hater. Nowhere were the Indian depredations worse than against the settlers of Texas.

On another occasion, a thoroughbred mare of the Short's was captured by the Comanches; when she refused to be ridden or driven, the Indians cut her ham-strings, and left the poor terrified and crippled animal piteously screaming and trying to get to her feet. Luke had to shoot her to put her out of her misery, and if he had not hated Indians before, he did afterwards—for the beautiful mare had been given to him by his Grandfather Brumley and was several months with foal.

1863 and 1864 were not good years to be on the Texas frontier, either. The war was looking badly for the South, and every available man was being called upon to join the Confederate Army. Wash and Hettie prayed that it would soon end, for their eldest son, John was sixteen.

Soon afterward, Luke Brumley was shot through the throat and face with a minie ball during a battle back east. When he was carried into the field hospital, the surgeon took one look at the broken teeth and jawbone sticking from the terrible wound, and said to a corpman, "Put him over there out of the way. He'll die anyway!"

Luke Brumley was still conscious, and as the doctor's words penetrated, he rose on one elbow and pulled his revolver. "I heard that, you son-of-a-bitch!" He said, as best he could with his torn mouth. "You'll work on me or I'll kill you right now!"

The startled doctor stood silent, watching the wounded man with the steady eyes, then motioned for the corpsmen to carry Luke to the operating tent.

Luke Brumley came home after he was able to travel with teeth and part of his tongue and jawbone gone, but he was alive. He would always have a problem talking.

The Shorts lost two wagon loads of wheat that year. One load was wheat they were taking to the mill to be ground into flour for their own use. The Comanches caught them out in the open and killed the mules pulling the wagon. The Shorts were badly outnumbered, and Wash left the team and wagon and got up behind Joe, while John and Joe held them off. They had killed a couple of Indians, but knew they must make a run for it. The Comanches chased them for awhile, but after Young wounded another Indian, they turned and went back to pillage the wagon.

The next day Wash and the boys returned to the site and found their wheat scattered all over the prairie, and their wagon burned. Two hams had been taken to eat from the now bloating mule carcasses. The next spring there was wheat growing all over the prairie where the Comanches had scattered the grain.

Wash and his sons returned home and loaded another wagon with wheat, and heavily armed, started for the flour mill again.

They made it to the mill without seeing Indians, but on the return trip were again set upon by a large band of Comanches. The boys could readily see there was no chance to get away without once more leaving the wagon loaded with sacks of milled flour, and making a run for it. Wash was stubborn and refused to leave the wagon, and told John, who was driving the team of horses, to go on. Wash dropped back and, by stopping his horse and aiming his rifle at the pursuers, managed to slow the Indians up. They knew there was only one shot in the rifle, but no Indian wanted to be the first to die. The three boys could see it was a losing battle, however, and Young and Joe dropped back beside Wash and stopped their horses. "Pappy," Joe said, "the team is getting winded, and we've got to leave the wagon and get out of here!"

Wash could see they were right. "All right," he said, "how are we going to do it?"

"Let's two of us shoot and see if we can put a couple of them down," Young said. "When we stop them, John will cut the team loose and jump on one of the horses and take off, then we'll all ride for the bluff."

Wash nodded. "You and Joe shoot."

The two brothers lined up on the Indians who suddenly began to scatter. With their shots, one Indian was knocked from his horse, and another of their horses fell with a rider. The three men then whirled their horses around and put the spurs to them. The little horse which Wash was riding wasn't much; in fact it was a worn-out Indian pony which had been left at their place during a previous raid. Wash got behind and one of the faster Indians came within arrow range and drove an arrow into the cantle of his saddle. The next arrow caught Wash in the back and went through his right lung. Another one hit him in the hip. Young swung around and dropped the Indian with a quick shot as Joe rode alongside his father. "Can you make it to the bluff, Pappy?"

Wash nodded.

"If the Indians don't give up—we'll have to jump the horses!" Joe said.

The bluff Joe was talking about, was a twenty foot drop into a deep pool of the river. And jump they had to, for their horses were badly winded and the Comanches were right behind them. They were able to get to the other side and get their horses on firm ground among a shower of arrows. No one was hit, but one of their horses got an arrow in the shoulder. Luckily the Comanches didn't try to cross the stream and pursue them, and the four of them were able to get their wounded father home.

Hettie used her surgical skills to help her husband. She cut out the arrowhead though Wash's chest, then soaked a silk handkerchief in whiskey and secured it to the cutoff end of the arrow. She drew it through her husband's chest to disinfect and cleanse the wound, then bound him up. The arrowhead on the other wound had struck a hip bone, and the boys had already removed it. Hettie must have known what she was doing, for Wash was back in the saddle in a few months, and lived to the age of seventy-eight.

The Short sons finally got through to the mill with a load of wheat that fall, and corn for cornmeal. After it was milled, they were able to get it home safely.

CHAPTER THREE

About the end of the Civil War, the Shorts were again getting ready to move. It was not a long distance move, but Wash had found a better location over in Cooke County. With sons, John, Joe, and Young, he loaded a wagon with tools and drove over to the new site. The four of them began building a much larger log house and outbuildings and corrals.

Wash had already sold their old place to a settler, and when the new house was ready, they moved Hettie and the other children east and got them settled. Just in time, too, for mother Hettie was soon to deliver a new face, the first born in Texas. It was a girl, and named, Belle Nannie, and in some strange manner, Hettie felt the little girl had come to replace the frail, old man who had started it all when he had stepped aboard a sailing ship in Liverpool, so many years before. Josiah Short had lived a full life and seen his children and grandchildren and great-grandchildren populate the new land. Now he was gone, dying quietly in his sleep. Another son was born and named George two years later.

Peace had not come to Texas with the end of the war. The northern carpetbaggers had moved into the country and tried to control everything. Will, the sheriff of Montague County, and his brother, Dan Brumley, had problems with the northern reconstructionists, and were shot down in cold blood by a lawless band of Jayhawkers. Shortly thereafter, their father, John Brumley was killed one morning when he stepped out onto his porch with a cup of coffee in his hand.

The younger children had missed much formal schooling during the Civil War when the country had been alive with raiding Indians, but Wash and Hettie had continued their personal instruction in reading, writing, and arithmetic. The old Blue Speller was still their basic school book, and the pages were dog-eared and worn. All the children could read and write and do their figures. Luke, was now eleven, Mary Catherine, nine, and Henry, six. Soon after moving to their new home, Wash started the three younger children in school. It was a small, one room log building with a pounded dirt floor in a settlement a few miles away. The school had a stable for horses, and the children rode their horses, carrying their lunches of biscuit and bacon sandwiches, and cold buttermilk in a stone jug.

Their first year the children had a earnest young man from back east as a teacher. He soon captivated Luke with classic novels he read to them, and it was here Luke developed his love of poetry which was to stay with him all of his life. Luke was to say much later, he learned much more with the young teacher in his first year than he did in the two that followed.

The next year the young teacher quit; he was unable to stand the loneliness of his position in such an isolated settlement. The teacher who replaced him was a huge, sour man of forty, and was ready to use his split bamboo cane for even an imagined infraction. All of the children hated him, for they soon came home with big, red welts upon their backs and legs. The easygoing Wash urged the children to not provoke the teacher. Hettie Brumley's temper prompted her to take the schoolmaster to task, but he ignored her. Finally, she and Young rode to see the schoolmaster in their buggy. When Hettie got nowhere trying to reason with the man,

Young pulled his six-shooter. He stuck it in the man's face and said, "If you ever touch one of my brothers or sister again, I'll kill you! Do you understand that!"

When the man didn't answer, Young eased back the hammer and said, "Do you understand what I'm telling you!"

The schoolmaster was white with fear, and he begged for his life. He promised not to whip the children again.

On the way home, Hettie was silent. She knew the wildness she had just seen in her son came from her side of the family, the Scotch-Irish Brumleys. They were a proud, honorable people, but if they ever felt they had been treated unfairly or badly, they were ready to kill. And they never forgot or forgave an injustice. Hettie and Luke promised never to tell Wash what Young had done.

Wash was a different man. He was a good husband and father, a mild mannered man who was very religious and read his Bible every day. Wash would fight if he had to, as during the Comanche and Kiowa raids, but he was a peaceful man who got along well with most everyone.

In the little settlement there was a church, and a preacher that held sermons on Sundays. The man was a roly-poly type who every Sunday got carried away and threatened his congregation with hellfire and brimstone, sweating and screaming at them, until at last the three older boys refused to go anymore.

Wash bluntly told them they would go. It was then John, Joe, and Young, told their mother if their father pushed the point, they'd all pack up and leave.

Hettie was in the middle, trying to keep peace in the family, but privately she sympathized with the boys. She considered the ranting preacher a lunatic and bore. "Where would you go?" she finally asked.

"We could join a trail herd, heading for Missouri," John said.

Hettie thought it over for a couple of days, then told her husband what the boys were planning. Finally, she told him that if he persisted, he'd lose all three boys, and put a barrier between them that might never heal, and Wash gave in.

But Young was soon in trouble, anyway. In the fall, as they were harvesting corn, Wash told Young to load a wagon with corn and take it to the preacher. Young, Luke, and Henry loaded the wagon and drove to the preacher's house. They backed the wagon up to the corn crib, and began to unload. The preacher and his wife were gone but his son, a big overgrown boy about Young's age was there. As Young and his two brothers started unloading, Young keep looking at the boy, thinking he'd jump in and help them, but the boy stood insouciantly by, leaning against the corn crib, picking his teeth with a straw.

Finally, Young's temper came to the surface. "Why don't you jump in here and give us a hand, you lazy son-of-a-bitch! After all, we're giving you the corn."

If Young was hoping to provoke the boy into a fight, he was mistaken, for he grinned and said, "Oh you boys are doing all right."

That did it. Young went after the preacher's son but he was already running to the house. Young walked back to his grinning brothers, and told them to reload the corn they had thrown into the shed. He then picked up the reins and drove to the nearest creek, where they let down the tailgate and dumped the corn.

It wasn't long before Wash learned of what they had done. He was furious, and got out his razor strap, but when he got ready to whip Luke and Henry, Young told his father he had been the one who had told them to dump the ears of corn into the creek.

"Well, it's you, then," Wash said and raised his whip.

"No, I don't think so, Papa," Young said, and walked out to

the barn where he already had his horse saddled, with his bedroll and war bag lashed behind the saddle. He kissed his mother as she followed him to the barn, then stepped into the saddle and rode off to live with Hettie's oldest brother. He was fifteen years old.

Luke was the next to go. The brutish scoolmaster had not whipped any of the Shorts after Young had threatened him, but he had another way of venting his anger. The schoolmaster had a son about sixteen years old. He was built heavy like his father, and outweighed Luke by at least eighty pounds. He began picking on Luke, and provoking a fight during their lunch time. Luke fought back, but it was no contest, and he often came home with a bloody nose or a black eye. When Hettie asked him what had happened he just said he'd been in a fight. She finally got the story of what was happening from Mary Catherine, and went to see the schoolmaster.

"I can't watch the children all the time," the man said.

"But that bully is your own son! He's the size of a full-grown man! He's several years older—and out weighs Luke by almost a hundred pounds!"

The schoolmaster just grinned at her. Hettie didn't know what to do. If she told Wash, he might punish Luke for starting the fights. If she told John or Joe, they might ride down and shoot the bully.

One day, out by the school corral where the horses were kept, the bully began beating Luke up again. When it was over, and the teacher rang the school bell, Luke went to the hand pump in the yard and began to wash the blood from his face. Henry and Mary Catherine both had jumped in and tried to help Luke, but the bully had slapped them out of the way.

Luke stood there in the school yard, as alone as a person could be. He couldn't keep on taking it, for he knew the bully would just keep beating him.

Across the street from the school was a house, and Luke had often seen a man there watching the fights. Today the man was leaning against the gate watching him. Presently the man motioned for Luke to come to him. Luke walked over and studied the man. He was young and had one arm in sling.

"You could shoot that porker," the man said.

"I've been thinking about it," Luke said, "but then I'd be in real trouble."

The cowboy nodded thoughtfully.

"What happened to your arm?" Luke asked.

"Oh, I been with a trail herd coming up from San Antonio way. Cattle spooked during a thunder storm, and my horse stepped into a hole and threw me. Broke my arm." The cowboy pointed to the house behind him. "My sister lives here. I'm just killing time until my arm heals, then I'll sign onto another drive. They're gathering up cattle all over down south. No money in Texas. Yankees got it all."

"Do you think I could get on one of those trail herds?"

"I don't know," the cowboy said. "How old are you?"

"Thirteen, but I'll be fourteen before long."

The cowboy stood looking at him. "I dunno."

Luke started to turn away and go back to the school, for he knew the schoolmaster would soon be out to get him.

"Wait a minute," the cowboy said. "You know you don't have to take that kind o' crap from that boy. Don't try to fight him with your fists. Hit him with anything you can lay hands on." The cowboy reached into his pocket and took out a strange looking knife. He pushed a button on the side of the hand, and a sharp blade snapped out. "Here, take this. You cut ol' fatty a little—and he'll cry like a baby. I guarantee it! World is full of bullies like him. You're small, and you'll be fighting it all your life. Just as well stop it right here!"

The cowboy showed Luke how to close the blade, then handed the knife to him. Luke put it in his pocket, just as the schoolmaster stepped outside and yelled at him.

That night Luke went out behind the barn and took out the switchblade. There was a little release lever which kept the blade from coming open in your pocket. He unlocked it and pushed the button, and the silver blade snapped out like the head of a rattler. The blade was sharp as a razor. Luke closed it and snapped it open several times, then closed the blade and locked it.

The next day Luke wondered if the bully would try to beat him up again. He had shown the knife to his brother, Henry, and the two of them waited. Finally they moved out behind the horse barn; that was where the schoolmaster's son was likely to catch him.

It wasn't long before he came, and shoved Luke down, daring him to get up and fight. Luke got up, feeling the power of the knife in his pocket. He stood there a moment, somehow knowing that this was a point in his life which was going to change things.

He drew the knife and pushed the button on the side, and the silvery blade snapped out. The bully saw the blade as he reached for Luke, but it was too late. Luke made a swipe from right to left, and the boy fell backwards. Blood stained his belly. He looked down incredulously at the blood. The razor sharp knife had sliced through the bully's shirt and trousers and opened his belly. Gray intestines were soon oozing out. The boy clasped his hands across his belly and began crying.

Luke stood in shock. He had only intended to cut him a little and scare him.

"Jesus! Luke," Henry cried, "you've killed him!"

Luke instantly knew he had to get out of there. He closed the blade of the knife, and ran for his horse in the corral. He slipped the bridle on, then the saddle, and swung up. Henry had the gate open. Luke stopped a moment and looked down at his brother. "Henry, I've got to go on the run. I . . I don't know when I'll see you again!"

Henry nodded, eyes like saucers, and closed the gate behind him.

Across the street the cowboy was watching him. Luke put his heels into his horses's flanks and went across to him. He took the knife from his pocket and handed it to the man. "Mister," he said, "I think I've killed him!"

"What you gonna do?" the cowboy asked.

"I don't know . . . leave the country, I guess."

The cowboy took an old bill and a stub of a pencil from his pocket, and turned and wrote something against the side of the gate. He handed the piece of paper to Luke, and said, "There's a big, tall, redheaded guy I know that's bringing a trail herd from Llano County, he was about a month behind us. Was I you, I'd take off and go to Red River Crossing. Ask them there at the store if the herd has come through yet. The cattle will have several brands, but their road brand is JD. If you find them, give Red that note. Maybe he'll take you on. A trail drive is a hell of a place to hide out for a man on the run."

Little girls were screaming in the schoolyard, and the schoolmaster was running toward the corral. "Good luck!" the cowboy said.

Luke dug his heels into the horse and went down the wagon road, and cut across country as he headed for home.

Luke was glad his father was gone; he knew he'd never understand. He told his mother what had happened, and asked her and his older sister, Martha, to get a bedroll, clothes, and some grub together. While they did that, he went to the corral and got his personal mare. She was half-thoroughbred and had been a gift from Luke's grandfather Brumley. Her name was Nellie, and Luke put his saddle and bridle on her.

He rode back into the yard, dismounted, and went inside. He took his short barreled Sharps and its scabbard. With ammunition for the Sharps in his hands, he met his mother and sister in the front yard. He lashed his bedroll and grub behind the saddle and turned to his stricken mother. "I"m sorry, Mama?" he said. "I've got to go!" Both his mother and Martha had tears in their eyes. "Luke," his mother said, "what's going to happen to you?" "I'll make out," he said, "I'll write when I can." He hugged them both, then pulled himself into the saddle and spurred his horse away. Once he stopped and looked back at them. They were still standing there watching him, hands shading their eyes. He knew they were both crying.

He headed west toward Red River Crossing, where there was a store. The trail drivers often bought a few staples and supplies while they waited to get their herds across the Red River, and then drive north into Indian Territory.

Luke was not quite fourteen that day in 1867. He didn't know his mother was pregnant; in October, she would give birth to another little boy, to be named, William. Though still of tender years, Luke was all ready a man in many respects. He had left home with heavy heart, and was now on his own.

He would not see his family again for almost sixteen years.

CHAPTER FOUR

Before the Civil War the term "cowboy" wasn't often used, and most of the men who handled cattle were Mexican *vaqueros.* There were a few Anglos in the cattle business in Texas, if you could call it a business. Some men owned longhorns, but there was little market for them, other than hides and tallow. Much of the meat from those killed for the hides was left for scavengers.

Then the cattle were forgotten for four years while most of the Texans went off to fight in the Civil War. When the men returned afterward, they found the land alive with wild, unbranded longhorns. The Texans were disillusioned and broke, and there seemed no money left in Texas. A few men had previously driven cattle to Louisiana, but that hadn't turned out well, for the most part. But there was a ray of hope; some enterprising spirits spoke of rounding up some of the half wild longhorns and trailing them through north Texas, Indian Territory, a corner of Kansas or Arkansas to Missouri. There were rumors cattle were being bought at the rail towns of Sedalia and St. Joe. The rumors had it cattle costing three or four dollars in Texas could be sold for up to forty dollars in Missouri.

The trail drives in 1866 were in most cases disasters. Cattle and men were lost crossing rivers, to stampedes caused by thunder storms and tornados, to rustlers and guerrilla bands of Jayhawkers left over from the recent war and to grass fires. The longhorns also carried ticks that caused splenic fever in other cattle. The longhorn had a resistance to the fever themselves, but when ticks were transferred to the local cattle, they quickly became sick. It was also called Texas fever, and soon the local cattle in Kansas and Missouri began to die. The local farmers, backed by a 1861 law prohibiting importation of diseased cattle, formed posses and confronted the Texas drovers and refused to let them go on. Many of the drovers turned their herds toward Baxter Springs, Kansas, and hoped for the blockade to end, but the grass around Baxter Springs was soon gone, and with winter, many of the cattle died. The defeated cattlemen returned to Texas. Some gave up in despair, but others were determined to find a way to the lucrative markets back east. They desperately needed money, and the big, rangy longhorns were their only hope.

Up in Kansas one man was working for their salvation, and he expected to make a lot of money himself. His name was Joe McCoy. McCoy talked the officers of the Kansas Pacific Railroad into giving him a good freight rate hauling Texas cattle east to the stockyards and slaughter houses. With an agreement from them, he began looking for a small town along the railroad in north-central Kansas. After making a survey of the region, McCoy decided on Abilene. Abilene was a hamlet with few farmers around to protest the passage of the trail herds. Also, Abilene could be reached by the trail drivers crossing the Red River north of Fort Worth and following the old Chisholm Trail through Indian Territory. Chisholm was an old half-Cherokee trader who had a post on the Arkansas River where Wichita is now located. Chisholm had for years driven his wagon loads of supplies south in his trading business, and the ruts of this trail could guide the trail herds north.

McCoy immediately bought 250 acres of land on the

outskirts of Abilene, and began to build cattle pens and install platform scales on which to weigh the cattle. He also got the railroad to put in switches and sidings for storing railroad cars and loading the cattle. Even before McCoy had his pens ready to receive cattle, he sent his representatives south in 1867 to meet with the herds he knew would be heading north out of the grass and brush country of southern Texas. McCoy, a northerner, was wise in the ways of the times. He knew the Texans were still smarting from their defeat in the Civil War, and hated to deal with Yankees. McCoy picked as emissaries Texans or other southerners, who knew cattle and would be acceptable to the Texan herd owners and trail bosses.

These emissaries headed south into Indian Territory, and began finding herds headed north. They talked to the trail bosses and told them where they could connect to the Chisholm Trail and follow it on into Kansas to Abilene, where they would be welcomed with open arms. Almost to a man, the trail drivers agreed to take the route and to sell to McCoy when they arrived at his rail yards.

Herds didn't begin arriving in Abilene until relatively late that season of 1867. But it was a beginning, and the Texans were heartened at having a market.

And it was in this same year a small, wiry boy not yet fourteen years of age rode his horse up to what would later be designated as Red River Station. He rode fast, always watching his back trail, certain that a sheriff was back there somewhere.

At the small store on the banks of the Red, Luke Short learned the brand he was looking for had not yet crossed. He bought staples with the few dollars his mother had slipped him, then turned his horse south, following the track of the herds that had come through the previous year on their way to Missouri.

Six days later, on the other side of Fort Worth, Luke found the herd carrying the trail brand he sought. He was apprehensive of seeking out the trail boss and asking for a job, afraid he would be turned down because of his age, so he passed on by, waving casually at one of the outriders until he was hidden in the dust of the drag. Finally, he decided to just began working the drag and somehow figure out how to ask for a job. His mare, Nellie, wasn't a cutting horse, but Luke knew she would soon get the drift of it.

The herd consisted of about 2,000 longhorns, and Luke soon was chasing steers back into the herd as they tried to break free and get away into the brush. The dust of the drag enveloped everything, and Luke soon tied his bandana up over his nose. Late that afternoon, when Luke saw the trail boss was calling it a day, he dropped back, and made camp in a nearby draw and hobbled his horse so it could graze. At the crack of dawn, he ate a cold breakfast, and as soon as the herd was on the move, he again joined it, taking up his position in the dusty drag. Occasionally he'd see another of the drag riders dashing in and out of the dust, but they apparently took him for one of their own.

One of the other riders must have become suspicious, for a tall man on a big roan horse rode up to Luke in the afternoon and motioned him to follow him.

They rode off to one side, clear of the dust, and the tall man rode alongside Luke and pulled down his bandana. "Who in the hell are you?" he asked in amazement.

Luke's heart was in his throat, as he thought. Finally he decided to use his mother's maiden name. "Brumley, sir, Jim Brumley."

"What are you doing back here?" The redheaded man said.

"Well, I'm looking for a job."

"Why didn't you ride up to me and ask for it, then?" the man asked.

"I was afraid maybe you wouldn't give it to me."

"You got that right!" The trail boss said. "What'd you do, run away from home?"

Luke nodded.

"Well, I suggest you turn around and go back to Fort Worth. That where you're from?"

"No, sir," Luke said. "I can't go back. I'm kinda on the run."

The trail boss grinned. "What did you do, run away from school?"

"I did that, too, sir, but I think I killed someone in a fight, and if I go back I don't know what they'll do to me. I'd sure like to stay here and help you. I'd work just for my grub."

While the trail boss sat there thinking about it, Luke pulled the note the cowboy back in Cooke County had written for him, and handed it to the man.

When the trail boss looked up he had a different look on his face. "How's Ed doin'?"

"He broke his arm in a stampede," Luke said. "He has it in a splint and sling. He's staying with his sister until it heals."

The trail boss turned and looked at the dust cloud that was moving north. "Can you help handle the horse remuda if I take you on?"

"Yes, sir!" Luke said.

"I got one of my own sons doing that job now, an' he badly needs help. I'll try you out for a week, and if you can handle it, I'll pay you fifteen dollars a month."

"Yes, sir!"

"What kind of a horse you riding there?" Red asked.

"She's half thoroughbred. She ain't really no cutting horse, yet, but she'll outrun anything you got."

The trail boss grinned. "We'll see about that one of these days. Come on, my son is going to be real happy to see you. One of your jobs is to gather firewood and help the cook when he sets up the chuck wagon in the evening."

"Yes sir," Luke said, and followed the man to the chuck wagon, where he piled his bedroll into the wagon with the other cowboys' gear. Then he was taken to the remuda where Red's son whooped and hollered and jumped around in a crazy dance when he learned he had someone to help him. The boss' son was two years older than Luke, and they were to become good friends.

The outfit consisted of fifteen men altogether: the trail boss, an older man for the cook, twelve cowboys, and the wrangler. Some of the men were Mexican *vaqueros* from Red's Texas ranch. The remuda had almost 90 horses in it, or five or six horses for each man. Four hours of heavy work was about all the horses could take at a time. The cowboys would come in at the end of that time, rope a relief mount, change bridle and saddle, then swing up and be off at a run. The remuda had a bell mare that was the leader, and after a week or so on the trail the herd would follow her pretty well. Luke's job was to help bring the horse herd along, to return any strays, and to assist the cowboys when changing mounts. He also had to hobble and keep track of the horses at night, and keep them from drifting too far. In the morning he had to help move them into a rope corral ready for the cowboys to pick their mounts. There wasn't a whole lot of time left for sleeping. In between all this, he helped the cook gather firewood whenever they crossed a creek where trees grew, and helped fill the water barrels lashed to the sides of the chuck wagon. The wood was carried on a cowhide slung beneath the bed of the wagon.

They were long, tiring days, but soon his sore muscles were behind him and he took pride in his job. After the first week Red stopped by one afternoon, and said, "You'll do, son."

Luke could not have been prouder. At the chuck wagon on that first night, Red had introduced him, saying, "Boys, this is

Jim. He's gonna be the second horse wrangler."

Luke did his job and was soon accepted by the crew.

The herd was held up at Red River Station; there had been rains up near the headwaters in Palo Duro Canyon and the water rushing through it became a raging torrent. Red knew it would be days before they could cross, and so he found grazing back a few miles, and they all settled in for a wait.

This crossing on the Red River went back a long way in history. It was said that Coronado had crossed here in 1540 in his search for the Seven Cities of Cibola. Later, in 1720, Sieur de Bienville, Governor of Louisiana, had sent Charles Claude Du Tisne to rout the Spanish who had two forts near the crossing. The French failed in the rout, but the Spanish soon abandoned the forts because of the Lipan Apaches. The crossing continued to be called Twin Forts, though the ravages of time and weather eventually crumbled the adobe walls of the forts.

White settlement of the Red River Valley was slow, but by the early 1850's there were perhaps fifty families at Spanish Forts; sometimes the settlement was simply called, "The Station." Later, it was called Salt Creek, then after the Civil war it began to be called Red River Station. The crossing led onto the old "Texas Road," or Chisholm Trail, across Indian Territory and into Kansas.

At the Station, a natural slope led down to the river, and the crossing cattle didn't have to fight a bluff. Later, men built a wide timber and log V-shaped barricade that forced the longhorns into river. A shelving sandbar ran out from the North bank, and the cattle didn't have to swim far before reaching it. Then it was just a matter of them walking out of the shallows into Indian Territory.

It took but four or five men to hold the herd as it grazed, so the cowboys had time to rest up and time to kill. Cards came out and they played poker on a blanket around the fire at night. They used matches for chips, but some of the men played for real money to be paid when the herd was delivered to the railroad in Kansas.

The cowboys had admired Luke's horse, Nellie, and wanted to know where it came from. Luke told them his grandfather had raised thoroughbred race horses, and the mare was part blooded. This finally led to a challenge. One of the cowboys said one of his string could beat Luke's mare in a race, and asked Luke what he had to bet. Luke declined, saying he had no money, but others encourged him to take up the challenge. Finally Luke said he'd bet twenty dollars to be paid when they got to Abilene, and the race was on.

While the cowboys made side bets, others measured off the course.

"Jim," the trail boss said, "I hope your horse is as fast as you say she is—because I've bet twenty dollars on her."

The cowboy got off to a fast start and was in the lead, but Luke soon overtook him, and was several lengths ahead at the finish.

The trail boss, pleased at winning twenty dollars, smiled, and nodded his approval. A couple of days later another herd came to the river and set up camp not far away. Red's cowboys soon challenged the other camp to race against Luke's Nellie. The course was again marked off and the bets made. Red loaned Luke twenty dollars to bet on himself, and the race was on. The eighty-five pound Luke on the blooded mare won again. Now he had twenty dollars in his pocket, and was, of course, the favorite of the cowboys who had bet on him.

One day the river was down enough to make the crossing, and the outfit floated the chuck wagon across with two big logs lashed on either side. Next went the remuda, and finally the cattle were pushed into the river. The crew heaved a sigh of relief when they were across.

Several days later their good fortune ended when a thunderstorm in the night spooked the cattle and they stampeded. All hands soon were into their saddles, as lightning flashed across the night sky. Luke helped the cook roll the cowboy's soogans in their canvas covers and stow them in the covered wagon, and then the sky opened up with rain. Luke and the boss' son had their hands full with the remuda and helping the cook. The earth trembled from the thunder and the sound of the herd's hooves.

When daylight came it was a bleak scene. There wasn't a horseman or cow in sight. Luke and the cook hitched up the team of mules, and as the cook drove north, Luke and his partner gathered up the scattered remuda and followed.

Several miles along the way, the cook spotted a steer standing with a broken leg. He shot it between the eyes with his pistol, and Luke and the cook dressed it and cut it into quarters for camp meat. Several miles farther along they met cowboys bringing in a bunch of cattle. They left the herd with a few men and went back out for more. It took all of that day and part of the next to round most of them up, but one man was missing. Red left most of the crew to guard the herd, then took several cowboys to look for the missing man. The searchers spread out, fearful the missing man had gone down and been run over by the stampeding herd. Finally one man spotted the missing man's downed horse, and the cowboy alongside with only burn marks on him; both horse and man had been killed by a bolt of lightning.

They stripped the saddle and bridle off the horse, and sadly lashed the dead man behind another rider.

Back at the chuck wagon it was a sad affair, and the cowboys ate in shifts, bedraggled and silent. Afterwards, they dug a grave, wrapped the dead cowboy in a tarp and buried him. Red said a few words from the Bible, and they built a fire on top of the grave, then drove the remuda across the spot to keep coyotes and prairie wolves from digging up the body. The cook had carved the cowboy's name upon a board, and drove it into the ground. The men that weren't guarding the herd sat silently for a moment on their horses, then rode off.

CHAPTER FIVE

The days settled into routine, one day much like another. The night herders would start the herd on the trail while the cook got a fire going and fixed breakfast. Luke was, at this same time, helping to get the remuda into a rope corral, and as soon as the cowboys finished a hearty breakfast of bacon, beans, with biscuits washed down with coffee, they began roping their horses for the morning. Then they saddled up to ride off and relieve the last shift of night herders, so they could eat. Luke and the cook packed things away, harnessed the mules and hitched them to the wagon, and the cook drove off. Luke and the boss' son herded the remuda off to the side to avoid the dust and gradually they worked ahead of the herd. The trail boss would lead the chuck wagon and the remuda, and sometime before noon would spur ahead into the distance and find a place for the chuck wagon to camp, so the cook could begin dinner. Red always tried to find a place with good grass. By the time the herd arrived dinner was ready: a pot of beans, perhaps steaks cut thin and fried in the Texas manner, biscuits and gravy, and coffee, of course.

While the herd rested or grazed, the cowboys ate, then roped fresh horses. They changed bridles and saddles, swung up, and began moving the herd out. The herd might make five or six miles in the morning, and that much or more in the afternoon. Red didn't want to push them too hard or they'd lose weight. Ten miles a day wasn't bad; some days they might make close to fifteen, and the cattle would hold their weight.

The afternoons were a repeat of the morning. They kept the cattle moving. Red and the chuck wagon would pull ahead in mid-afternoon, and find a camping place, hopefully close to a creek or spring, where the cattle could drink and the cook could fill the water barrels lashed to the chuck wagon's side. The cook would start his supper fire, and repeat it all over again with little change to the menu. If he was feeling good, perhaps he might cook up a rice and raisin desert. If there wasn't a storm or stampede, the next day would be exactly like the last.

Sometime after they crossed the North Canadian river, in Indian Territory, they met a man riding south. He turned out to be a Texan hired by Joe McCoy. The man told them about the pens that McCoy was building in Abilene, and that he was prepared to pay a good price for the first herds that arrived. Red nodded, his grey eyes not showing the relief he felt. The buyer's rep had supper with them, then in the morning rode south. Before he left Red told him McCoy could count on his herd, if he was offered a fair price. The crew became excited, talking about what they would do when they reached Abilene, though it was still a long way to go.

It wasn't long before they crossed the Cimarron, and headed for Jesse Chisholm's old trading post on the Arkansas River. Most of the trail herds that year had started out late; they had heard rumors there would be a rail town to receive their cattle, but they hadn't known where it would be. Now they knew, and they pushed on toward Abilene.

After crossing the Arkansas River near Chisholm's post, they began their last leg. Another week and they would be at Abilene. Sometime in the middle of August they had the town in sight. Red had already ridden ahead the day before and talked to McCoy. The railroad wasn't quite ready to begin shipping cattle east, so they picked out a spot to hold the herd where the grass was good and it wasn't far to water. Red was very pleased with his talk with McCoy, and now he welcomed the chance to let the cattle graze on the grass and fatten up.

Some of the cowboys were anxious to go into town, and Red let four or five go in at a time. Luke finally got to ride in and look around. There wasn't much to see, but new buildings were going up and there were plenty of groceries for the cattlemen to buy. Red had gotten a small advance from McCoy, and he bought groceries from the store, and fresh vegetables and eggs from the farmers nearby. Some of the farmers were protesting the Texas cattle, worrying about the Texas fever, but others seemed glad to be able to sell their produce and fresh eggs, home cured bacon and hams.

During the first week in September, Red had word from McCoy to begin bringing in the herd to be weighed. The cowboys would cut out three or four hundred at a time and move them into the pens by the freight yard. McCoy had a platform scales which could weigh perhaps twenty head at a time, then they were put into holding pens.

Longhorns matured slowly, and at eight or more years could weigh between 1,000 and 1,600 pounds. They were hardy beasts, tall and rawboned, carrying a lot of bone and hooves and horn, but given the chance, could put on weight fast. The three weeks they had been able to graze on the lush grass south of town had done wonders for them. Red grinned to himself as he watched McCoy's men weigh the cattle. One bunch of twenty steers averaged almost 1300 pounds each. At a cent-and-a-half a pound on the hoof, that figured out to almost twenty dollars apiece! In Texas, Red had rounded up 750 longhorns of his own. He then bought on credit, 1300 more from a friend for five dollars apiece, with the understanding that he would split all money that he received above thirteen dollars a head with the rancher. Red figured it had cost him a little more than a dollar a head to get the longhorns to Abilene. They had been extremely lucky, and lost less than a hundred head.

The check Red received from the sale amounted to a little less than $33,000. When he deducted the almost $11,000 he owed his rancher friend back in Texas, he had over $20,000 left.

Red paid off the crew, giving ever man a month bonus. He even paid Luke full wages of thirty dollars a month.

With the bonus, Luke had ninety dollars, plus the money he'd won on the horse races. It was the most money he'd ever seen, and he felt rich.

They had made their sale at just the right time, too, for half a dozen herds that were behind them all came in at once. The Kansas Pacific didn't have enough cars to the haul all the cattle, then the market back east was bogged down, and the price fell. Such were the vicissitudes of the cow business. Approximately 35,000 head of cattle were delivered to Abilene during that late season of 1867, but despite the down turn in price, the Texans were enthusiastic. They took their money and went home, and planned on bigger things for the next season.

With the herd disposed of, the cowboys went to town, and got haircuts and baths. They bought new clothing, boots and hats, and crowded the restaurants and saloons. They walked along the boardwalk street with their new Stetsons tilted at a angle, their huge roweled spurs jingling, completely at peace with the world, the past hard three months of work already forgotten.

Red had also sold off the remuda, save for the horses the cowboys would ride back to Texas. He had sold the chuck wagon as well, but the buyer had agreed to let the cowboys use it until they were ready to head south.

One day Red took his son, the cook, and Luke, to town with him to do some chores and buy a few groceries. After they had loaded their purchases, Red took them all into a saloon for a drink. Luke and Red's son felt pretty grown up standing at the bar and drinking a whisky toddy.

In the back of the saloon several gambling games were in progress. When Red walked back and bet a few turns at the faro table, Luke followed, and was at once fascinated. Dealing out of the faro box was an elegant man dressed in a ruffled white shirt, black string tie, and black suit. Across his embroidered vest was a heavy chain festooned with huge nuggets of gold leading to his watch. He was a tall, good-looking man with a goatee, and in his tie was a large diamond pin.

Red played for an hour, winning some, and then began to lose. He cashed in his chips then, and the four of them had another toddy at the bar, and left, but Luke would forever afterward remember the fashionably dressed gambler. He thought how grand it would be to dress that way and to make money in such a manner. He learned later the gambler's name was Dick Clark, and he was a high roller who gambled in Kansas City and St. Louis and on the steamboats during the winter season when the cowtowns would dry up.

There, that day, Luke made a promise to himself someday he'd be such a man. He could not know it then, of course, but he and Dick Clark would often cross paths in the years ahead, and they would become close friends.

Red planned to finish up his affairs in Abilene in a few days, and he and his son would take the train east to St. Louis. At St. Louis they'd buy a few presents for the rest of his family, then ride a steamboat down the Mississippi to New Orleans. From New Orleans they'd either take a stage to Texas, or perhaps get aboard another steamer headed for

Galveston. Red asked Luke what he planned on doing. Luke said he thought he would ride back to Texas, when the rest of the cowboys were ready to go. He then asked Red for a job for the 1868 season.

"Sure," Red said, "you look me up at the ranch and I'll put you to work when we start rounding up cows. Fact is, why don't you just go on down there to my ranch, and stay with us this winter. You can pay for your grub by doing chores around the place until we start getting a herd together."

After Red and his son left, Luke and the cook camped around the chuck wagon with the rest of the cowboys. Most of the cowboys were in their late teens or early twenties, and most of them had to get rid of the money that was burning a hole in their pockets.

With the promise of a job in the spring, and a place to stay for the winter, Luke bought a Stetson, new boots, and a heavy winter coat. He bought cartridges for his Sharps, then splurged on a deck of playing cards. His father had thought cards were the Devil's instrument, and had never allowed them in the house. Luke had watched the cowboys play, and now he and the older cook played penny ante as they waited for the cowboys to get rid of their money.

That wasn't long in happening, and one day they all put their grub onto a pack mule, and turned the chuck wagon over to the new owner. Luke wrote a letter to his mother, telling her he was doing fine. The next morning the cowboys headed south.

It was a gay, carefree trip home for them. They had made a little money and had a good time in Abilene, and now were headed home. On the way they ran into a party of belligerent Southern Cheyennes, and it looked hairy for awhile, but they were well-armed and after a few shots without anyone hit, were able to go on their way.

By the end of October they were deep into Texas, and the

cowboys drifted off one by one to their homes. Luke and the cook, who was a steady employee of Red's, continued on into Llano County where Red's ranch was located.

CHAPTER SIX

For the next two years Luke worked for Red, and helped gather longhorns and trail them north to Abilene. He learned a lot from the others, and as he grew, he hardened until he was tough as the rest of them and outgrew the wrangler's job. When they delivered the longhorns to Abilene in 1868, they found a completely different town. Joe McCoy's Drover's House was finished and filled with cattle brokers, drummers, and herd owners from Texas, some with their families, enjoying the business and social life as they waited for their herds to show up. There were plenty of saloons and gambling and dance halls to keep the cowboys happy, also whorehouses, clothing stores, boot shops, and what-have-you. The businessmen knew how to woo the Texans, and named their saloons, The Alamo, Lone Star, Bull's Head, among others, and many of the bartenders and gamblers were either Texans or from the south. It was a wide open town, and though farmers were moving to the area, and still screaming about Texas fever the longhorns brought, their protests were pushed aside. None of the businessmen wanted to kill the golden goose.

The following year, Red sent two herds north. He delivered one to Abilene, but sold the other herd of mostly cows to a man starting a ranch in Nebraska. Luke elected to help drive the herd north and ended up in Ogallala. Afterward

41

he took the train back east to see Kansas City, then St. Louis for the first time. He rode down the Mississippi on a grand stern wheeler, then made his way back to Llano County.

The next year he again went north. After the herd was delivered, and the cowboys were again camped around the chuck wagon enjoying the bright lights of Abilene, a cowboy from another camp rode up and said, "I heard there's a man named Jim Brumley in this outfit. Thought I'd ride over and see if it was any of my kin."

Every one looked at Luke, who studied the man, and saw that it was his uncle Ben, from Montague County, Texas. Ben had supper with them, then later Luke and Ben walked out away from camp to talk. Ben told Luke the schoolmaster's son that he'd knifed, hadn't died after all. The doctor had sewn him up, and he was doing fine. Luke was relieved to know there wasn't a murder charge hanging over his head.

When Luke went back to Texas, he didn't stop by and see his family, though it was only a short distance from Red River Station. There is no doubt that he felt he had disgraced himself and his family by cutting up the school bully. He also doubted that his father would be forgiving. There was something else to consider: Luke knew when he had learned enough, and had the money to pursue professional gambling—his family would not approve. He felt like the family black sheep. If and when he went home, he wanted to be successful. It was something that drove him for the rest of his life.

When Luke told Red and the crew his real name, they just laughed. There were several of them going by names other than their own, for various reasons, but Luke was still called Jim by Red's crew for as long as he was with them.

Although Luke was still a boy in years, the hard life of a cowboy had hardened him into tempered steel. The Mexican *vaqueros* on Red's ranch in Texas had taught him the art of *reata,* and he became an expert in throwing the braided rawhide rope, and forefooting and heeling longhorns during the branding and cutting season.

In his off hours he continued to practice with the cards. To his delight, he finally began to realize that he was a natural born "card counter," and in a card game which gave an edge in remembering the cards already played, he invariably came out ahead. He practiced with his pistol, now a Colt .45, for he knew that a small, mild-looking man like himself would forever be challenged in the rough and lawless frontier towns that would be his home.

At nineteen, he had his growth, stood about five-foot-six, and weighed possibly one hundred and thirty pounds. He had a short, straight nose, pale grey eyes, and light brown hair with a touch of ginger to it. He was a handsome young man, and when he got to town was all ready beginning to show the fastidiousness that was to mark his dress in later years.

Luke helped take a herd of cows and young heifers on through to Ogallala, Nebraska Territory in 1871, and stayed there to deal cards in a gambling house. He spent almost two years between the Colorado mining camps and around the tough Nebraska cattle towns. The summer of 1873 Luke went to Kansas City and looked the town over. He immediately like the looks of the high rollers that frequented the thirty or more gambling houses. One of Luke's favorite gambling halls was Potee's Faro Number Three. It was owned by a grand old Southern gentleman, named Bob Potee. He was tall and slender, and wore gold-rimmed spectacles. He was always faultlessly dressed in a long-tailed black gambler's coat, with a ruffled white shirt. Like most of the high rollers, he wore an expensive $1,500 European-made Jürgensens watch in his vest pocket, and the gold nugget watch chain, which attached it to his vest, must have cost a year's wages. In his tie was a huge diamond pin. On the street he wore a silk top hat and carried a gold-headed cane. He was a proud man, and had the reputation of a completely honest gambler.

He was absolutely fearless, and could handle himself in any kind of confrontation. Luke soon heard the story of a customer who had lost a great amount of money at Potee's faro table. The man pulled out his pistol and threw down on Potee, accusing him of cheating. Potee had assured the man he was in an honest game, and told him to put away the pistol and sit back down if he wanted to continue the play; if not, he was invited to take his business elsewhere.

"Like hell I will!" The man cried, and eared back the hammer of his pistol.

There is some confusion about exactly what happened after that, for the eye witnesses were diving out of the line of fire. Two shots rang out and the overhead lamp went out with a crash of glass. When another lamp was brought in, Bob Potee was still sitting in his chair, both hands still on the table, and sprawled across the table was the body of the tinhorn gambler, a bullet through his heart. "When the table is cleared, we'll start with a fresh deck of cards." Potee said calmly.

While Luke was in Kansas City he met many of the high rolling gamblers who were already legends. The Senate was run by a father and son team, the Findlays, and there was Clayton Maltby, Tom Wallace, George Frazier, and John Evans, among others. Luke also met the owners of the Marble Hall, Joe Bassett and Colonel Rickets. Joe Bassett was another honest gambler, and was to become a close friend of Luke. Joe was a brother of Charlie Bassett, later, the first sheriff of Ford County, Kansas. Charlie would be Luke's ally during the Dodge City Saloon War of 1883, and Joe Bassett's Marble Hall would be his home away from home as he fought to reinstate himself.

Now, he was just beginning to meet these legendary

gamblers, and he was awed to be in such distinguished company. Luke's run of luck at the Marble Hall got Joe Bassett's attention, and after asking Luke about where he had worked before, Bassett offered him a job dealing. Though Luke was doing all right as a free lancer, he recognized the fact his luck would certainly change, and that he could get a lot of valuable experience in a high-class place like this. Luke took Bassett's offer, and it was the beginning of a long and warm relationship.

Sometime in the fall of that year, Luke began hearing of the enormous amount of money being made by buffalo hide hunters out in central Kansas. The talk was a good shot could keep a couple of skinners busy, and make a hundred dollars or more a day. Luke decided to give it a try. He said goodby to Joe Bassett, and took the train for Dodge.

CHAPTER SEVEN

The experts estimated that before the real slaughter for buffalo hides began there were between twenty and thirty million buffalo ranging the plains and mountain valleys of the west. After the completion of the Union Pacific Railroad there were two great herds: the northern herd ranged from the Powder River country on into Canada, and the southern herd frequented the area between the South Platte and the Arkansas River, and on into the Texas Panhandle and New Mexico.

Before Dodge City was Dodge, it was called Buffalo City. There was another post office called Buffalo, so to avoid confusion, the businessmen elected to rename the town in honor of Colonel Dodge. The army post already named Fort Dodge was five miles east of the town.

Somewhere around 1871 a new tanning process was developed back east, and the tanneries were able to handle great quantities of buffalo hides for leather and belting and such. Previously, the market had mostly been for buffalo robes, but now, with a new market for various kinds of leather, men flocked to Dodge to get into the business with the coming of the railroad.

In the past Luke had killed a few buffalo for the meat, and had once traded several raw hides to an Indian woman for a tanned robe. Now he found himself in Dodge, looking for a way to get into the hide business.

One evening in a saloon he met an Irishman called Paddy. Paddy owned several mule teams, and wagons. He had previously worked for the Sante Fe Railroad, grading various stretches of the right-of-way with his teams and equipment. Now Paddy had lost his contract, and was sitting around Dodge with his teams and wagons, wondering what to do. The two men were excited about the talk of the money to be made in the hide business, and by the time the evening was over, they decided to go together and become hide hunters. Paddy would supply the mules and two wagons, Luke would supply the buffalo guns, lead, powder and provisions and they'd split the profits.

While Paddy reworked his two wagons to haul hides, Luke began to get their gear ready. They needed axes and shovels, pots and pans, skillets, a Dutch oven, coffee pot, and water kegs. Luke traded his short barreled Sharps in on two longer and heavier barreled Sharps of .50 caliber. He bought lead, powder and primers, and a reloading and bullet-casting set. For staples he bought plenty of flour, dried beans, coffee, sugar, potatoes, dried apples and peaches. He had also talked to men he knew who were already in the hide business. They advised him to take plenty of powdered poison to dust the hides, or the insects and small animals would render them worthless in a short time.

For entertainment, if they had time for such a thing, Luke had a couple of decks of cards, and several books.

Luke and Paddy decided to hire two skinners to start with, so Paddy recruited two men who had worked for him grading on the railroad right of way. One was a Mexican called Jose who said he'd skinned a lot of longhorns in Texas. The other man was a fellow Irishman who was a good worker, Paddy said. Luke bought both ripping and skinning knives together with sharpening stones, and soon they were ready to leave Dodge.

Luke had often seen big herds of buffalo north of Dodge on

cattle drives, and suggested they try out the country between the Buckner and Pawnee Rivers. Ideally, they would find a good place on a creek, where they could build a dugout and set up camp. Paddy put the two hired skinners to driving the wagons, and Luke and Paddy took the lead on horseback. The partners had guaranteed the skinners $50 a month and their keep.

Two days out of Dodge they came upon a camp site along a small creek which ran into the Pawnee River. They had been seeing buffalo, and decided this spot was ideal. Behind the creek was a low bluff, and they unloaded the wagons and hobbled the mules, and began to dig a shelter into the side of the bluff. There were plenty of trees along the creek to roof the dugout, and to use for firewood. They built a rock fireplace and within a few days had the roof covered with sod. The roof was vented to allow the smoke from the fireplace to draw, and they were settled in.

Paddy had bought enough lumber to build a large smokehouse. He also had a lot of salt and brown sugar and crocks to sugar cure some of the hams. There was a good market back east for smoked buffalo tongues, and for cured hams. Most of the buffalo hunters didn't want to take the extra time to cure these delicacies, but Paddy said he knew how to do this. Since Luke was an excellent shot, it was decided that he would do the shooting, and the two hired men would skin the buffalo. Paddy would take care of all the buffalo tongues and as many of the hams as he could handle.

They had noticed small herds of buffalo as they moved out to Pawnee River. Now they were ready to begin gathering hides. One morning Luke mounted his horse and rode off to look for a herd. He soon found perhaps a hundred in a draw about two miles away. He tied his horse a good distance from the buffalo and began to stalk the animals with the wind in his favor. When he had crept to within 150 yards, he found a little hummock that gave him cover. Luke had a cartridge belt, and loose cartridges in his pocket. He took off his coat and used it for a shooting pillow, his cartridges lined up and ready beside him on a piece of canvas. He had sighted in his Sharps at camp, and knew it was shooting right on the target. He had talked to many buffalo hunters, and he knew what to do. Now he picked out a sentinel bull which seemed nervous. He shot him through the lungs and watched him stumble around coughing blood, then go down. Some of the other bulls looked stupidly at the downed animal, sniffing him. Luke reloaded and methodically began to drop the other bulls. Everytime a bull on the outskirts of the herd moved off, Luke shot him. He took his time, firing slowly so that his barrel would not overheat too quickly. He shot twelve or so buffalo, poured water from his canteen down his barrel, then opened the breech to let the water out. When the barrel had cooled, he swabbed it out with a slightly oiled rag, reloaded and began to shoot again.

Twice more Luke had to stop and cool his barrel, but kept at it until finally the herd spooked and he lost his stand. He stood up at last and looked down at the huge forms spread out before him. He picked up his empty brass cartridges and walked down among them. Several weren't dead, and he shot them between the eyes with his Colt.

Luke started counting them, then lost count, but he knew there more than sixty buffalo lying around him. Soon he saw one of the wagons coming. It stopped on a little rise, waiting, and Luke beckoned them to come.

Paddy and the skinners were awed when they saw all the big, shaggy forms. Paddy grabbed Luke and danced around in a circle, letting out howls like a wolf. Luke was no stranger to death. He'd seen cattle killed in stampedes, horses with broken legs which had to be shot and he'd seen men killed many times, but the sight of all the buffalo lying with their eyes glazed in death bothered him in a strange way. They were out here to kill buffalo and make money, but still he was bothered.

The Mexican skinner had also agreed to cook, so while Paddy, Luke and the other Irishman began to skin, the Mexican built a fire and made a pot of coffee.

They all wore huge leather scabbards with four knives—two ripping knives and two curved bladed skinning knives. With the buffalo on their sides, they made a cut around the neck, then ripped down the belly from vent to neck. Next they ripped out the insides of the legs, and with their curved skinning knives flayed out enough of the hide to get a good purchase. With a mule hooked to the purchase, they peeled the hide off as you'd skin a rabbit. The four men were slow to start, but learned quickly and picked up speed.

They worked hard, and by dark had all the buffalo skinned. A full grown buffalo's hide weighed around a hundred pounds green, so it was hard work. There were sixty-five of them, and they were rolled and loaded into the wagon. Then the men cut out the tongues, and also butchered a young bull for camp meat. They loaded as many hind quarters onto the wagon as Paddy thought he could smoke, then headed for camp. While the cook got supper, the other three man stretched out the buffalo hides, flesh side up, and cut small slits around the edges and staked them to the ground to dry. The hides would be turned every day until they were completely dry. In five or six days, they would lose half their green weight and be cured enough to stack.

It was hard, brutal work, and dirty, too. The four men wore tightly woven duck pants and coats and soon these were covered with blood and fat from the skins. The hides had to be dusted with poison to kill the insects which infested them, but many of these insects got onto the men, and with lice, the men scratched constantly.

Despite this, they were making money, and that was what they had come for. They settled into a routine, with Luke doing all the shooting, the skinners skinning and carrying the raw hides back into camp, and staking then out to dry. Paddy was busy with his smokehouse. He had the buffalo tongues hanging in the smokehouse curing, and the hind quarters were cut into three pieces each about the size of large pork hams. These pieces were soaked in large crocks in a mixture of brown sugar, salt, and a little saltpeter to help hold the color. Later they were taken out of the solution and hung in the smokehouse and smoked. When they were properly cured, Paddy sewed them up in light canvas covers, and stored them.

One thing the men soon noticed about the herds: the bulls all stayed together in separate groups, and the cows and calves in theirs. The only time the two groups mixed was during the mating season. There were always more bulls than cows, and this was probably because the Indians and whites both preferred cow meat to that of bull. Also, the Indians preferred the cow hides because they were easier to tan.

There were other hide hunters around and, when they were working the herds, sometimes were not far apart; the booming of the big .50 Sharps was heard continuously during the daylight hours. The rules of hunting were simple but strict. The first man who began working a herd was given priority rights, just as though he owned them. Seldom were there problems. Any man passing to windward of a herd while another hunter was trying to stalk that herd was in for trouble. A rifle bullet might whistle by, letting him know he was out of order.

A good skinner could skin twenty or more buffalo a day. When skinners were hard to find, the owners of an outfit might have to pay up to twenty-five cents a hide to have buffalo skinned.

Here in the late fall of 1873 the buffalo hides were prime.

The weather was cold enough so there were no flies to bother the meat as Paddy cured hams and smoked tongues. It was a full time job for him, as he also had to turn hides that were drying, and have supper ready for Luke and the two skinners.

When the wind was right, the smell of rotting carcasses drifted over the prairie, and buffalo wolves must have thought they were in heaven. It hurt Luke to think of all the meat going to waste, but they could only handle so much. Many of the hide hunters didn't bother at all with the meat, except for taking the tongues.

One night Paddy just shook his head sadly as he thought about all the people the meat could feed. He told of the Irish who had died of starvation in his native County Cork of Ireland during the potato famine. Out of his family, his mother and father were dead, and four brothers and sisters. Paddy had stowed away on a sailing ship and landed in New York, but there was little work for a young unskilled Irish boy, and he had joined the army and served along the Rio Grande during the Mexican War.

When Paddy figured he had a load, they all pitched in and loaded both wagons with hides. They also loaded the smoked buffalo tongues and hams, and Paddy and the Irish skinner would each drive a wagon to Dodge to sell.

Luke and Mexican Joe would ride out and look for another herd, and soon the big .50 Sharps would be booming again.

A couple of bad blizzards kept them in their dugouts for a few days at a time, then they were back to their routine again. They occasionally had to move camp, following the herds when they moved. The *Wichita Eagle* that winter said there were thousands upon thousands of hides being brought in to the railroads, and that there was a line of buffalo hunters' camps all the way from Dodge, clear into Colorado. The paper estimated as many as two thousand men were engaged in the hide business.

General Sheridan, when he was commander of military headquarters in San Antonio, once told the Texas legislature they should give the buffalo hunters a medal for killing buffalo. He went on to say:

"These men have done more in the last year to settle the vexed Indian question than the army has done in the last thirty years. They are destroying the Indians' commissaries and it is a well known fact that an army losing its base of supplies is placed at a great disadvantage. Send them powder and lead, if you will; but for the sake of lasting peace, let them kill, skin, and sell until the buffaloes are exterminated. Then your prairies can be covered with speckled cattle, and the festive cowboy, who follows the hunter, as a second fore-runner of an advanced civilization."[1]

The Texans, who had borne the terrible Commanche and Kiowa raids for decades, raids in which they'd lost hundreds of settlers and had their children killed or made slaves, had applauded General Sheridan. Indeed, most of the people on the frontier felt the same way. It was all right for liberal easterners to cry for the poor Indians' plight, now that they had killed or driven all their Indians off, but the frontiersmen still had to deal with the present.

The buffalo hunters were destroying the Indians' commissary, all right. It was estimated more than 100,000 hides were brought in from just around Dodge in that year.

Luke and Paddy continued to do well. Luke had always been an excellent shot, and as he learned more about the buffalo, the more success he had. He now used two and sometimes three rifles on a good stand, rotating them to keep the barrel from over-heating.

It wasn't all drudgery, sometimes in the evenings they'd sit around the fire after supper and put on a show. The rule was, that each man would have to perform in some manner. It was up to him as how to do it. Mexican Joe would dance or sing sad Mexican songs, Paddy sometimes would tell stories of his battles during the Mexican War, at Monterey and Saltillo, or might do the Irish jig. At one point they had a Negro skinner who could dance like the wind and play a harmonica at the same time. Luke, when his turn came, invariably quoted poetry from Shelley, Lord Byron, or perhaps read a passage from Shakespeare. You would think that such a rough bunch of men would have been bored, but they always sat enthralled as he spoke, and asked for more. Luke always carried his favorite books with him, and in this way transformed himself from a frontier boy with very basic schooling into a well-read gentleman who would one day fit into any sophisticated group. Indeed, many years after Luke was dead, Bat Masterson would report:

"He (Luke) was nothing more than a white Indian . . . twenty years later he was an exceptionally well read man. He could write a good letter, always used good English when talking and could quote Shakespeare, Byron, Goldsmith and Longfellow better and more accurately than most scholars. To the burning of midnight oil was due the transformation . . . from the white Indian when first I knew him."[2]

Masterson was a little off on his timing, Luke's transformation had begun as soon as he made enough money to afford the books which fascinated him.

Luke and Paddy followed the herds and continued to make good money. Sometimes they had six or seven skinners working for them, and one man who was camp tender. He guarded the camp when they were all gone, and helped Paddy turn the hides and tend the smokehouse fires.

The Medicine Lodge Treaty with the Indians was made back in 1867. The treaty specified the Indians would not raid north of the Arkansas River, and the whites would not hunt buffalo south of this line. This seemed like a clear cut solution, but didn't work in practice, for the Indians soon broke the rules whenever they saw fit, and, of course, so did the buffalo hunters. With the scarcity of buffalo, the hunters began casting eyes on the plains south of the Arkansas. It was known there were vast herds south in Indian Territory and on into the Texas Panhandle along the Canadian River.

During the spring of 1874, a bunch of hide hunters gathered in Dodge, and spoke about the scarcity of buffalo. Soon some of them proposed to band together with their outfits as protection from the Indians, and head south across the Arkansas River. They would setup headquarters on the Canadian River, where they knew there were big buffalo herds. As they talked A. C. Myers, an old buffalo hunter who had also cured and smoked meat around Dodge, said he'd take his outfit and also a stock of merchandise to sell to the hunters at Dodge City prices. Then James Hanrahan, who hunted on a large scale, joined in with his considerable outfit.

The party found a site on East Adobe Walls Creek, not far from Old Adobe Walls, the trading post built by William Bent around 1844. Then Rath and Wright, hide buyers and store owners, showed up and erected a building to join Myers and Leonard in buying. Hanrahan put up a building and started a saloon. There didn't seem to be many Indians around, and the hunters began to go out and set up their hunting camps. Among all these men were two young hunters, Billy Dixon, and Bat Masterson.

About the time the buffalo migration began to arrive, several hunters were killed, scalped and mutilated. As word spread, the hunters began forting up at Adobe Walls. On the morning of June 27, 1874, Adobe Walls was attacked by 700 or more Indians.

The Comanches were under the leadership of Quannah Parker, the half-breed son of Cynthia Ann Parker, who had been captured during an Indian raid in Texas many years before. Lone Wolf led the Kiowas, and Stone Calf and White Shield led the southern Cheyennes.[3]

The battle at Adobe Walls has been told and retold. Basically, the small group of buffalo hunters stood off the horde of warriors, losing only a few men.

While the battle was being fought at Adobe Walls, small, Indian raiding parties were scouring the countryside for other buffalo hunters and their camps. Luke and Paddy were raided and Mexican Joe and another skinner were killed. All but two of their mules were killed and their camp and hides destroyed. While Luke and Paddy and the other men were pinned down, they killed several Indians, but they were out business.

After the raiding party left, they buried their two comrades, and limped back north to the Arkansas River, and headed for Dodge.

When they finally arrived, Luke bought new clothes and took a long bath. Afterwards he burned all of his old clothing.

He and Paddy settled up with their remaining crew, had supper, and adjourned to a saloon. After a few drinks, Luke told Paddy they'd made good money, but he was tired of killing buffalo and being filthy and scratching vermin all the time.

"My thoughts exactly," said Paddy. "I hear the Santa Fe's laying track again out in Colorado. Think I'd rather go back to grading railroad right-of-ways than fighting Indians south of the Arkansas. "What're you going to do, Luke?"

"I'm not sure." Luke said.

The two partners had a good relationship and enjoyed each others company, but now they shook hands and went their separate ways.

Meanwhile a party of men had ridden south to Adobe Walls to relieve the besieged buffalo hunters, and the army moved out to pursue the hostile Indians. It wasn't long before the hunters were back on the buffalo grounds.

Luke had been thinking about the string of hunting camps, and the needs of the buffalo hunters. He bought a team of mules and a wagon, loaded it with staples, a few luxuries, and barrels of whisky, then set off to the south.

Luke found his rolling store to be very popular with the buffalo men, and he soon was making more money than he had as a hunter, and without all the brutal, filthy work of skinning and handling the insect ridden hides.

Much later, Wyatt Earp remembered he had first met Luke Short in a buffalo camp when Luke was selling whiskey out of a barrel. Luke also met Bat Masterson about the same time. These three men were to become fast friends, and often worked together at various gambling halls during the next ten years.

Luke continued to service the scattered camps of buffalo hunters west and south of Dodge until sometime in 1875, then he went back to Dodge and sold his team and wagon. He had been hearing about the gold fields up in the Black Hills of Dakota Territory, and one day he took the train east and north to Kansas City. After spending some time relaxing and visiting with Joe Bassett and other friends, he caught the Union Pacific west across Nebraska to Sidney, Nebraska. He spent the rest of the winter dealing cards.

CHAPTER EIGHT

A terrible battle was shaping up between the United States and the Sioux and Cheyenne Indians. The United States Army had wanted to get all of the western Indians on reservations for some time, but some chiefs like Crazy Horse, Spotted Tail, and Red Cloud had forced the U.S. Government to abandon its forts along the Bozeman Trail. In 1868 two of these chiefs finally agreed to leave the white wagon trains alone on their way to Oregon and California, and to quit harassing the railroad that was being built west. In return the whites agreed to stay out of the Black Hills and an immense strip of land extending from the Platte to beyond the Big Horn Mountains. This agreement was called the Fort Laramie Treaty of 1868, and was signed by Red Cloud, Spotted Tail and various commissioners for the United States. Crazy Horse and Sitting Bull refused to sign anything, saying the land was all theirs, and to hell with the white eyes!

Things went along pretty well for a time, but the whites had been casting covetous eyes upon the Black Hills. A few prospectors had sneaked into the hills, and found a little gold. Soon there were more whites beginning to work their way to the hills. Some were killed by the Indians, and the army was told to keep the whites out.

Then, for reasons known only know to the politicians, and Generals Sherman and Sheridan, Custer, in 1874, was ordered to lead an expedition into the Black Hills, ostensibly to survey the area, and to look for a spot for a fort that could be used to keep white prospectors out. Actually, Custer's job was to learn if there was, indeed, a substantial amount of gold in the area. Custer had several prospectors with him to make this determination, as well as newspaper reporters to publicize the discovery.

Gold was found, and Custer sent a reporter's dispatch immediately to the nearest telegraph. Prospectors soon began to pour in the area and the army was unable or unwilling to force them out.

General George Crook, who had done wonders down in Arizona with the Apache depredation, was ordered north, and given command of the Department of The Platte. He was at first ordered to keep the prospectors out of the Black Hills, but then, things seemed very vague in Washington.

First, the railroad barons had been scamming the government for years. During the Civil War they had stolen the treasury blind with cost-plus work that would have brought shame to a downright thief. After the war, as they drove west, they perfected the scam; if it cost $30,000 a mile to build the rails, they would charge $50,000. Besides all this, they were being given millions of acres of land as an inducement. In 1869, Josiah Perham, who had started what would eventually be the Northern Pacific Railroad, went belly up. Financier Jay Cooke, bought the bankrupt company at fifteen cents a share. Cooke, a crook like the rest of them, ran a fraudulent construction company, and bribed Congress-men, as well as anyone else who had influence. When Ulysses Grant needed funds for his 1872 reelection, Cooke helped out with several million dollars. Then, in 1873, a financial bloc led by J.P. Morgan and Company, set out to destroy Cooke and his empire. Cooke had applied for a $300 million loan from the government to help finish the Northern Pacific

Railroad, Morgan spread the rumor that Cooke's credit was almost worthless. Congress backed off, and Cooke's construction stopped. Not long afterward his bank failed, and other firms began to go under. Trusted officers of large corporations skedaddled with much money and disappeared. Then the stock market fell, prices dropped to the bottom, and the country moved inexorably into a depression, the worst this country had ever seen. People stared dumbly at one another. Thousands were out of work. There was real panic.

So, what was the country to do? And what had all this to do with the Sioux-Cheyenne problem out west. Just this: Grant and the politicians needed something that would take the peoples' minds off their problems. What better than to have a gold rush in the Black Hills? The gold rush in California had helped give the north specie to get her factories going and win the war.

So, when George Armstrong Custer found gold in the Black Hills of Dakota Territory the following year, the Pooh Bahs back east knew they had a winner. There was only one problem: the government had signed a treaty with Sioux and Cheynne leaders back in 1868 that gave them the whole of the Black Hills and all the country in between and beyond the Big Horn Mountains. The United States of America had never before let a treaty bother them too much, and so, the machinations began.

It wasn't hard for the Indians to understand just why it was that as soon their reservation was found to amount to something, they must leave it and let the white man move in. The Indians could see that still more miners would be moving into the Black Hills, and the army troops would do nothing about it. You didn't have to fast upon the mountain to see a vision of what was happening. The white man intended to steal the Black Hills.

Red Cloud and Spotted Tail had both been back east and

seen the white man's power; they knew that if it came to an outright battle, the Indians would, in the end, lose. They both hoped that somehow they could get a fair settlement if they had to give up the Black Hills, so when a party of commissioners came for a meeting, they asked for $7,000,000. The white commissioners would probably have settled for that amount, but unfortunately, the translator got mixed up and put the figure at $70,00,000. The whites flatly turned it down, and Spotted Tail and Red Cloud stalled, and waited for better times.

Sitting Bull and Crazy Horse accepted that they would have to fight, and they sent some of the lesser chiefs to the Spotted Tail and Red Cloud Agencies in northwestern Nebraska to get warriors. Many of the Indians that had come to the agencies were disillusioned with the rations they had been promised, as well as with the boredom. They readily caught their horses, armed themselves from hidden caches, and slipped away. Finally there were hardly any able-bodied men left. In fact whole families went in great spirits, as if on a summer outing. They looked forward to being free once more and hunt buffalo, and live in the old way.

General Crook had made great use of Apache scouts against renegade Apaches in Arizona. Now, here on the Platte he had been recruiting Arikaras, [also called Rees] Hidatas, Crows, and some Shoshones as scouts against the Sioux, Cheyenne, and Arapahoes. These tribes had long been enemies anyway. Such scouts in the field began to tell Crook that the Sioux and Cheyenne were slipping away from the reservation in great numbers. The Indians began killing prospectors and freighters and taking their weapons and supplies. Perhaps four hundred white men had been killed before the Army of the Platte took to the field.

When Crook sent word to Sheridan and to Sherman, they got their heads together, and soon had a plan. Crook was to go to Cheyenne and begin getting his army ready. Two other strong columns were also directed to take the field—one under General John Gibbons, with troops from Montana camps—another, under General Alfred Terry was to start from Fort Lincoln.

On June 17, 1876, Crook was engaged by the Sioux and Cheyenne. Fifty-seven of Crook's men were killed or wounded. But for his Indian scouts warning, his troops would have been drawn into a trap by Crazy Horse, and a great many more killed. Very likely the shock of how close he had come to being wiped out, did something to his thinking. In any event, he immediately pulled back and turned around to regroup. Crook, a seasoned Indian fighter with more than 1000 soldiers, 260 Indian scouts, plenty of supplies, plus a party of well-armed miners, was reluctant to move forward, yet that was what he was supposed to do—drive the hostiles up against Gibbons and Terry. What he did, was dally around in the Tongue Valley, hunting and fishing and enjoying the scenery. Much of Captain John Bourke's book, *On the Border With Crook,* tells of the trout catching contests there on the Tongue River. One reads it in amazement, wondering what was in the mind of Crook, the old Indian fighter.

At this same time, up at the mouth of the Rosebud, Terry, Gibbons, and Custer were making plans to keep the Indians from escaping. The three general officers figured the hostile Sioux and Cheyenne numbered no more that 1,500 fighting men. Lonesome Charley Reynold, the experienced white scout, together with Custer's favorite Ree scout, Bloody Knife, told the three generals they believed there were too many Sioux and Cheyenne to fight. The officers all dismissed their words out of hand. Later it was proven that the hostiles had more than 3,000 warriors.

The rest is history. Custer disdained Terry's offer of four troops of the 2nd Calvary, and also refused Gatling guns, afraid they would slow him down. The 7th Calvary, 611 strong moved out, up the Rosebud.

On the night of June 24th, the column reached the spot on the Rosebud where the hostiles had crossed a few days before as they headed up the Little Bighorn. Custer, instead of resting his hard-pressed men, opted for a night march. He was still afraid the hostiles might get away.

The next morning, Custer made his biggest mistake when he divided his force into three units. He took five troops of the 7th Calvary, and went north to outflank the hostile's camp, sending Major Reno, in the center, and Captain Benteen, with his men to the left flank. Soon Reno was in trouble as the Indians chased him back across the creek, killing his men right and left.

Shortly, Custer was in the most trouble of his impetuous life, as the warriors boiled out of camp in his direction. It was probably then that Custer realized how wrong he'd been. He turned his men around and rode toward the top of a small hill, but his men were falling, and still the Indians came. As the survivors gained the top of the hill, Crazy Horse swept up over the far side with his followers. In perhaps twenty minutes it was all over.[1]

The hostile Indians had outwitted everyone from Crook to Terry, and of course the arrogant Custer, who had been wiped from the face of the earth. The sad thing about it, was that he'd taken so many good men to their deaths. The Indians had won the battle, but not the war. What they didn't realize, not then at least, was that a horrified country would now unite behind the army, and would spare no expense, depression or no depression, until every Indian was killed or back on the reservation.

CHAPTER NINE

Many of the Indians had been slipping out from the Red Cloud and Spotted Tail Agencies, and some of them had just grown tired of the agency and wanted to have a good time and live the old life again. Joining the hostiles they had a chance to count coup and kill their longtime enemies, the Crows and Shoshones. Some brought along trading items and planned to exchange these items for robes and furs which could be sold for relatively high prices at the agencies. Many of these people wanted to see Crazy Horse and Sitting Bull, and maybe fight with them against the white man. Some of the younger men, living on the reservation, had never taken their places in a war party, and needed to prove themselves. Others merely went along to visit with old friends, and to enjoy the summer weather, to ride wild and free again without the white eyes telling them to do this and do that.

Immediately after the battles on the Rosebud against Crook, and after Custer and his men had been killed at the Little Big Horn, the Indians sensed the indecision seeming to paralyze the American Army. The big Indian camp on the Little Big Horn soon split up in many groups, and roving bands of Indians continued to kill miners and freighters wherever they found them.

Luke had spent most of the winter in Cheyenne dealing in the Inter-Ocean Hotel. The Inter-Ocean also had a big saloon and gambling hall, and was owned by Ed Chase and his brother, John. Ed Chase soon turned the management over to his brother then went on to Deadwood, in the Black Hills, to open another saloon and gambling hall that would be popular with the gold miners.

With the weather getting better, Luke was looking for something different to do, and it was about this time when he met Major Thornburgh again. Luke had once won a horse race in Sidney, Nebraska that the Major had bet heavily upon. The Major had been stationed at Sidney Barracks. Since that time, whenever Thornburgh ran into Luke, he would stop and talk and buy him a drink if that was possible. Now Thornburgh was getting ready to go in the field again to try and run down some of the renegade Sioux and Cheyennes that were killing miners and freighters all over the area. Thornburgh was a progressive thinker, and had learned long ago that the local frontiersmen were far ahead of army troops when it came to scouting and dispatch riding. Thornburgh asked Luke to join up with him, as either a scout, or a dispatch rider.

Luke thought about it for a couple of drinks, then told Thornburgh he wouldn't mind riding dispatch, if the pay was any good.

Thornburgh said he was authorized to pay ten dollars per day for these two positions. He said if Luke took the job, he'd be carrying dispatches between himself and General Crook's Command. The army would also furnish him good, strong horses, ammunition, and grub. Luke accepted, and within a week, he was with Major Thornburgh and his troops out in the field. He soon made a reputation for himself that endured, and was still being talked and written about well into the 1900's.[1]

In the summer of 1876, Luke was carrying a dispatch from General Crook to Major Thornburgh through hotly contested country. Crazy Horse knew Crook's army had been beefed up, and his policy was not to pit his forces directly against Crook's, but to harass him with hit-and-run tactics which the Indians, by nature, were superbly fitted to do. Luke had encountered hostile Sioux and Cheyennes before but had always gotten away on his big, strong army horse. Sometimes, when Luke ran into fresh Indian sign, he might hole up during the day, and travel during the night. On this day he was set upon by five Sioux warriors as he crossed a narrow valley. He put the spurs to his horse, and was pulling ahead, when an Indian bullet took his horse in the tail. The bullet entered the tailbone and shattered the vertebra. The poor animal immediately went down, squealing horribly in pain. Luke was thrown hard, but quickly got up, for he knew that his pursuers would soon be onto him. He shot his poor mount with his six-shooter, and tried to get his Winchester repeating rifle out of the saddle scabbard, but his dead horse had fallen on it. The lead Indian was now almost onto him. Luke took aim with his revolver, and knocked the Sioux out of the saddle. When the man tried to get up, he shot him again, then desperately, he began trying to work his rifle from under his dead mount.

Later, he would say something must have given him supernatural strength, for he got the rifle free, and jacked a cartridge into the chamber, hoping the sights hadn't been knocked completely off. Luke then lay down behind his dead mount. He rested the rifle barrel across the horse's belly and tried to calm his pounding heart. The closest Indian was coming fast, carrying a lance. Luke took a few deep breaths, then let them out, put his front sight squarely upon the man's chest, and squeezed the trigger.

The man was bowled from the saddle by the heavy .44-40

slug, and Luke turned toward the next Indian who was coming from the side. But after seeing Luke shoot the warrior out of the saddle with a rifle, all three of the Indians wheeled their horses around and tried to put a little distance from him. The closest one was frantically quirting his horse away when Luke's front sight lined up on the middle of his back.

Luke's shot knocked him from his horse. He moved to the other two targets, and killed both of them without missing a shot.

Luke reloaded with trembling fingers, still lying behind his dead mount. He waited for perhaps fifteen minutes, to see if the there were more Indians in the vicinity. There was nothing in sight or sound, only the gentle stirrings of the branches of a nearby tree, and the sound of a crow telling his friends there would soon be food for all.

Luke watched the five Indian ponies. They had stood around in confusion for several minutes, looking back as if expecting their owners to come for them. Finally they drifted off to a patch of good grass and began feeding. Luke watched them for some time, knowing that it would be hard for a white man to catch one. Indian horses and dogs didn't like the smell of a white man any better than animals which were attached to white men liked Indian scent.

By the time a hour had gone by, Luke believed there was little chance of another band of Indians being close. As he watched the Indian ponies, he knew they had been pushed pretty hard, for they were busy grazing. He believed that he might have a chance of catching one.

He took the bridle off his dead horse, then the saddle, and carried them over to a small thicket. Then he untied his Mexican reata, thankful of his decision to bring it from Dodge in his baggage. Leaving the saddle and bridle, he began working his way toward the Indian ponies. As he neared, they slowly moved away, not fast, but keeping an eye on him. He was relieved they had been ridden hard and were hungry.

There were several different colors among the five ponies, but the largest was a paint, a beautiful animal that kept a close watch on him as he worked his way closer. Luke finally put his rifle down, and slowly slipped closer. He would try for the first horse he could get within range of, but he wanted the paint. Luke thought perhaps the Sioux had captured the beautiful horse from a Crow or Shoshone. Every time Luke got almost in range, the horses moved away. He was afraid they might ease their hunger soon and take off.

It was late afternoon before he got his chance; he had gotten to within twenty-five feet, and had his loop made. With the paint's back to him, he made his throw, holding his breath as the braided reata shot out. But it was good, and tightened up as the horse lunged forward. Luke dug in his heels as the paint pulled him across the meadow. The other horses took off, and left him fighting the paint. The horse was like any other used to a rope; as soon as it began to choke itself, it eased up, standing there trembling.

Luke talked soothingly to the animal, and finally got it somewhat used to his smell. Finally he was able to throw a half hitch over the paint's nose, then lead it back to where he had left his rifle. Presently he was trying to saddle the skittish pony. This took another hour.

He tied the paint to a small tree, and went out to check the dead Indians. He took a few things from them, a buckskin medicine bag with some pretty green rocks and other things in it, a buckskin vest heavily worked with beads and porcupine quills, a pretty bone necklace. The two rifles were old, worn single shots. Luke did take the lance from the one Indian, though it would be a chore to carry. The bow and arrows he left, though. He had enough to carry, now.

Finally he got the trinkets tied behind the dispatch bags, and mounted. The long, sharp tipped lance he had stuck into the ground. Now, he rode up to it and pulled it free, then moved off to the southeast.

It was a moonlit night, and Luke kept moving toward the point where he thought he might cut Thornburgh's trail. Early the next morning he spotted a Indian on the far side of a flat valley. He moved out of sight, and presently saw another Indian, then several more. He was almost at the point of slipping away, when he heard a mule bray. Presently a column of soldiers rode into view, followed by the civilian packers and their mules. Luke took out his revolver and let off a shot.

Instantly the Crow scouts turned and spread out toward him, coming fast on their little ponies. Luke sat his saddle and waved his hat, and the whole command turned toward him. The scouts soon recognized him, and rode up in a cloud of dust. They looked at his paint horse, then at the lance he carried, and grinned, for they knew it was Sioux.

As Luke and the scouts rode back to meet the column, the head Crow scout was trying to trade the beautiful paint from him.

"Problems?" Major Thornburgh asked, as Luke dug Crook's dispatch from his bag.

"There was for awhile," Luke said, then told Thornburgh and his officers the story of the fight.

When Luke told them where it had taken place, the Crow scouts immediately persuaded Thornburgh to go there as it was little out of their way.

When they at last moved into the valley where Luke had been ambushed by the Sioux, the Crows were ahead of the column quite some distance. Presently they could hear the yelling and kiying of the scouts when they found the dead Sioux.

By the time the column came up to the scene, the Crows had stripped the bodies, scalped them, then cut them limb from limb. The head Crow scout tried to give Luke the bloody scalps, and when he refused them, they tied them to their rifle barrels and careened around on their tough little ponies with as much enthusiasm as if they had killed the Sioux themselves.

When they camped that evening, Thornburgh gave half of the Crows permission to go after the Sioux ponies, and soon they were off, immediately picking up the trail across the meadow where Luke had roped the paint.

At supper that evening, Thornburgh poured whiskey for Luke and the officers, and insisted that he tell the complete story a second time.

Afterward, Thornburgh said, "Luke, I think you earned your pay yesterday!" He was silent for a moment, then asked, "Do you know what it costs the government to put this Army of the Platte into the field?" When Luke shook his head, Thornburgh said, "About a million dollars a day!"

By the time it was dark, the Crows were back with the horses they had gone after.

"Bloodthirsty bastards!" Thornburgh said to Luke, "but by God, we'd be lost in the field without them!"

They went on the next day, but missed the hostiles Crook had directed them to close with. They found only the remains of a party of prospectors that had been caught and butchered by the Indians.

* * *

The story of Luke's fight was passed around to other calvary and infantry troops, and soon was generally known at Deadwood and Custer, and Sidney Barracks, in Nebraska. The story always bought Luke drinks in a saloon where his face was known, and, of course, he had the esteem of all the friendly Indian scouts who knew him.

Luke was soon laid off as Crook and the others forced the hostiles back onto the reservations. With winter coming on he headed back to Kansas City, to warm up and spend the rest of the winter with his friends. He worked for Joe Bassett at the Marble Hall dealing faro, and bought new books and caught up on his reading. His exploits with the Sioux had made the rounds, and those gamblers who recognized him, didn't usually start trouble at his faro table. He was learning a reputation like that didn't hurt in the gambling trade.

When spring came, he decided to go to Dodge City. During the previous year the Sante Fe Railroad had built more rail sidings, and put in cattle pens. Because the quarantine line for Texas cattle had again been moved farther west, Dodge was situated perfectly for the cattle trade. They had had a good year in 1876, and now this season promised to be even better. The businessmen of Dodge had made a lot of money with buffalo hides; now they went after the Texans' cattle trade wholeheartedly.

CHAPTER TEN

In the spring of 1877 there were sixteen saloons in Dodge City gearing up for the coming cattle season. All the businessmen were expecting the total number of cattle to be shipped to far exceed the previous year. The buffalo were gone. A few old hunters sometimes brought in a few hides, but no big money could be made anymore. There was, however, another industry that had been spawned by the hide hunters; this was the gathering of the bones from the slaughtered buffalo. Bone buyers in Dodge bought them for eight to ten dollars a ton, and many a nester kept his family in food with proceeds from the buffalo bones he hauled into Dodge in the years that followed. Most of the buffalo bones were ground into fertilizer, but some were made into buttons and bone china, and even the horns and skulls were polished up and sold back east.

Luke found his services as a gambler much in demand when he stepped off the train in Dodge. Probably his slow Texas drawl and his familiarity with herd owners, trail bosses, and cowboys accounted for much of this. Although Luke was not yet twenty-four, he was an old-timer, for he had been in Abilene when it was just starting as a cowtown. In fact, some of the cowboys he had known still called him Jim. All this was known by the business owners, who were, for the most part, northerners. These men knew the Texans were still smarting from the South's defeat during the Civil War, and from the high-handed treatment of grafting carpetbaggers and outright Jayhawkers who had come south after the war and controlled many aspects of southern business. Consequently, the saloon owners tried to hire Texans or at least Southerners, as bartenders and gamblers. Many of the saloons' names reflected this urge to cater to the Texans, and make them feel at home. Some of the saloons were: the Alamo, Saratoga, Nueces, Lone Star, Stock Exchange, Sample Room, and Crystal Palace. The Long Branch, which was to become the premier saloon and gambling hall in Dodge, was named after President Grant's summer home at Long Branch, New Jersey. Certainly this fact was not made known to the Texans by it's original owner, Robert Wright. The Long Branch began to make its reputation the following year when Chalk Beeson bought the building, and he and his partner, William Harris, began managing the business. But in 1877, Beeson and Harris were operating the Saratoga Saloon, and they apparently were able to hire Luke first, because Harris had met Luke at Joe Bassett's Marble Hall in Kansas City. Joe Bassett's brother, Charlie, was also the present Sheriff of Ford County, and was one of the "Gang", a term being applied to the Dodge faction which favored an open town that would appeal to the drovers and their cowboys who would be spending their money freely.

The Gang was for law and order, but they had observed the way the previous cattle towns had gone downhill as soon as they tried to keep drinking, and gambling, and prostitution away from the fun loving cowboys. The cowboys came up the trail and fought deadly river crossings, tornados, Indians, rustlers and stampedes, and by God, they were determined to have a good time when they finally reached a town and their work was finished.

Much of the Gang's opposition wanted their business, too, for some of them were in the saloon business as well as other establishments which made their money from the cowboys, but they would have rather had *all* the business. Many of the opposition were German-Americans, and they tended to stick together in their opposition to the Gang. Herman Fringer owned a drugstore, and had been appointed County Clerk in 1873. Frederick Zimmerman was a gunsmith and sold guns and other hardware, and John Mueller was a bootmaker. Larry Deger was Dodge's first City Marshal after incorporation; he weighed almost 300 pounds and was always against the Gang.

The so-called Gang consisted of James (Dog) Kelley, Beeson and Harris, Bat Masterson, and his brothers, Ed and Jim. Also Wyatt and Morgan Earp, and of course Wyatt's friend, Doc Holliday, as well as Charlie Bassett, among others. Luke was soon included in this group as he got to know all of these men. It might seem strange that a Texan would get along so well with these men, for all of them, with the exception of Holliday, were from the North, but Luke never judged a man by his origins or his politics; in fact, he thoroughly detested his fellow Texan, Ben Thompson, and his troublemaking brother, Billy.

Luke was soon drawing the Texans into the Saratoga Saloon and Gambling Hall in droves. One other reason the Saratoga was so popular was that the owner, Chalk Beeson, always had music at night. It was here Luke really got to know Bat Masterson and Wyatt Earp, and it was a friendship that was to last the rest of his life. Masterson and Earp were pretty fair gamblers and they began to deal in some of the town's gambling halls in their spare time.

In that summer of 1877, Ed Masterson was assistant city marshal of Dodge. Mayor Dog Kelly eventually fired the marshal, Larry Deger, and replaced him with Ed. In the fall election, Charlie Bassett could not, under the law, run for another term as Sheriff of Ford County. Bassett supported Bat Masterson for sheriff, and Bat won that position. He immediately appointed Bassett as his under sheriff. Charlie Bassett soon had two positions for Ed Masterson asked him to also serve as Assistant City Marshal.

Luke roomed at the Great Western Hotel owned by Dr. Samuel Galland, and his wife. Mrs. Galland was in charge of the kitchen and served fine meals. Luke paid eight dollars a week for room and board. Although Dr. Galland was a prohibitionist and didn't serve liquor in his establishment, he and Luke became great friends. Possibly because they both loved poetry. Indeed, though Dr. Galland was on the other side of the fence politically, he supported Luke during his difficulties in the Saloon War of '83.

The cattle season of 1877 brought more than 200,000 longhorns to Kansas that season. Most of them came to Dodge.

Sometime in October things began to wind down, and it was about then a young man from Austin, Texas came to the saloon where Luke worked, and they became friends. His full name is lost, and we know him only by the initials of T. J. He had come up the trail with one of the last herds more as a lark than out of a need for money, for his family was wealthy. Luke was about ready to make a swing around to Kansas City, then back to Ogallala or Sidney, Nebraska. T. J. was interested in going with him and asked Luke if he knew something exciting for them to do during the winter. Luke told T. J. about all the Indians around the Spotted Tail and Red Cloud Agencies. Most of the hostiles had been whipped back onto the reservations after the winter campaign of the previous year. Luke knew many of the Indians were frustrated by the high prices charged at the agency stores.

Most of the Indian agents and storekeepers positions at the agencies were political plums for President Grant's friends and supporters. The Indians were aware they were being cheated and had long resented it. Luke told T. J. that he knew the two of them could go into the Spotted Tail and Red Cloud area with a couple of wagon loads of trading stock and make a lot of money.

"What's exciting about trading pots and pans and needles and cloth goods to the Indians?" T. J. asked.

"Well," Luke replied, "we could make wages doing that, but the Indians will immediately want whiskey, too. That's where the real money could be made."

"That's against the law, isn't it?" T. J. asked.

Luke nodded, then grinned. "You just asked me about doing something exciting. We'd not only have to watch that the Indians didn't lift our hair—but we'd have the army after us if they ever found out."

"How much can we make?"

"A lot! I've talked to a lot of Indians, and without exception, they rate the most desired things in the world in this order: whiskey, horses, guns, and then women."

"If this is that dangerous," T. J. asked, "why're you willing to chance it? You've been making a good living here."

"For ten years I've been working hard and risking my life trying to get a bank roll big enough to open my own gambling house and have enough to bank my own games . . . "

T. J. didn't say anything for several minutes, until finally he looked at Luke and said, "I'm willing to chance it, if you are."

Luke nodded. "You come from a wealthy family. Why would you stick your neck out for more money?"

"That's just it," T. J. said. "I'm always taking money from my old man. Just once I'd like to go home with a pocketful—and show him!"

Luke talked Bill Harris into letting him go early in the fall.

In return, he promised Harris that he'd return and manage the gambling part of the business for them the following spring. Soon afterwards Luke and T. J. packed their gear and war bags, and caught the train to Kansas City. Then the two men went on to Omaha, Nebraska.

CHAPTER ELEVEN

In Omaha Luke and T. J. got a hotel room and spent several days taking care of business. First Luke went to the buffalo hide dealer whom he'd previously talked with. The northern herds were getting very scarce, and the dealer still bought what he could of dried flint hides, but when Luke told him he was interested only in the price of Indian tanned buffalo robes, the dealer's eyes lit up. He said he'd pay ten to twelve dollars each for a good, winter robe tanned by the Indian women. Luke told the dealer he'd soon be receiving a load of first class buffalo robes.

The next stop was a wholesale store, handling everything from pots, pans and skillets, to needles, thread and bolts of cloth. Luke already had his list made up and began to pick out various items he knew the Indian women desired. In the grocery department he bought a large amount of coffee, brown sugar, molasses, corn meal and flour. He also picked out bulk dried fruit, and a few other items he thought the Indians would want.

The next day they went to a wholesale liquor distributor, and Luke bought several barrels of clear grain alcohol, and many cases of empty pint jugs.

The day after that they had all their purchases delivered to the freight yards, then moved out of the hotel and were soon on the train heading west to Sidney, Nebraska.

After arriving in Sidney, the partners saw to the unloading of their freight, then got a room in a hotel where they left their personal gear. At the local livery, they bought two wagons with canvas covers. They also bought teams and harnesses to pull the wagons, and two saddle horses.

That evening while in a nearby saloon, Luke and T. J. were having a drink, and Luke asked the bartender if there was anybody around who raised good Indian dogs.

The bartender looked at him a moment, then asked, "Going north?"

Luke nodded. "My partner and I are heading up around the Niobrara River. Going to start up a cattle ranch. Lots of Indians around there, I hear. We'll need a good Indian dog to keep them from stealing us blind."

The bartender said, "Well, I know just the man." He took a piece of wrapping paper and began to draw a map. "Old man lives about ten miles north of town. Used to be a helluva Indian scout. That's all he does now is train Indian dogs."

Early next morning, Luke and T. J. awoke and washed, then carried their bags down to the restaurant and ate a hearty breakfast. They went to the livery stable and had the liveryman hitch up their teams of horses to their wagons.

When everything was ready, they tied the saddle horses to the tail gates of the two wagons, and drove to the train station to load their freight. By noon, all was loaded, and with their saddle horses tied behind the wagons, they drove north out of town.

From the map the bartender had given them, they found the log cabin of the old dog man. He was a gaunt, grizzled man and had at one time broken a leg which hadn't healed properly and he limped badly.

"Yeah, I got lotsa good Injun dogs, I tell you, mister," he said to Luke's inquiry. "No Injun is gonna sneak up on you with one of my dogs!"

Luke and T. J. followed him back to a big yard fenced in with poles set on end. Here he had his kennels and dogs.

T. J. was fascinated. He had been born and raised in Austin, Texas and had not really known how things were out on the frontier. "How do you make what you call an Indian dog, Dad?" He asked the old man.

"It's pretty simple," the old man said, "you jest get him to hate Injuns."

"Tell me," T. J. persisted. Luke stood aside thoroughly amused.

"Well, I got me a family of tame Injuns livin' down by the creek there in that holler. They help me 'round the place and keep an eye on my cattle. I pay the Injun kids a little to come up here and switch the pups every day. They don't hurt the dogs, none, but Mister, I tell you no Injun is ever going to sneak up on your camp if you got my dogs around! That's all there is to it."

T. J. looked at Luke. "That's it?"

Luke nodded.

The old man took them around and let the different dogs get used to them. After a while he said, "Stay here. I'll send my Injuns kids up." He limped off down the creek.

Presently all the dogs began raising a racket. Luke and T. J. looked over the pole fence and saw two Indian boys coming up the slope perhaps 150 yards away. There was no way the dogs could have seen the boys.

T. J. looked at Luke in amazement.

Luke touched his nose. "Sure, they smell them. We had them back in Texas when I was a kid."

All the dogs were now at the end of their chains, snarling and wild. The old man sent the two boys away, and grinned at Luke. "Good dogs, huh?"

"What do you want for them?" Luke asked.

"A hundred apiece. You pick them out."

"Is that bitch the mother of those young dogs over there?" Luke asked, pointing.

"Yeah, that's this bunch's mother."

"I'll take the mother and one of her grown pups." Luke said.

"Oh, I'd have to have a little more for the mother," the old man slyly said. "Three hundred for the two."

"Two-fifty."

"Well, all right," the old man agreed. "Say, why don't you camp here tonight? Take the dogs on a chain, and let 'em get used to you. Say, do you gentlemen play poker?"

Luke and T. J. unhitched their horses, put them in the old man's corral, and watered them. They fed them oats, and then cooked supper over a fire beside one of the wagons, after inviting the old man to eat with them. They fed the dogs, then tied them to the wagon for the night.

After supper they followed the old man into his cabin, and indulged him a game of poker. Luke threw away enough good hands to make sure their host ended up winning a few dollars.

They said good-night, spread a tarp down beneath the wagons, and unrolled their bedrolls.

"You know, partner," Luke said, "I don't think the Indians are going to sneak up on our camp and take our hair very easy with those dogs."

The next morning they had an early breakfast, and put away their bedrolls. Afterward, they harnessed the teams and hitched them to the wagons. With the saddle horses trailing, and the two dogs in the wagon with Luke, they said good-by to the old man and headed north.

Five days later they found a perfect hideaway north of Camp Robinson; it was in a grove of trees overlooking a stream. They took axes and cut enough poles to make a tent frame, then erected the large tent they had purchased in

Omaha. They stacked their possessions and trading stock in one corner of the tent, and pulled the empty wagons behind and parked them. After hobbling the horses and putting them out to graze, they began to make their camp comfortable. In front they built a rock fireplace to cook on, and settled in. It was a pretty campsite, isolated, but still not more than fifteen miles from the Red Cloud Agency. The Spotted Tail Agency was located perhaps thirty-five miles east of Red Cloud.

The following week Luke and T. J. began to mix up their booze. They brought up a barrel of clear water from the creek, and mixed it with grain alcohol until it was about 65 or 70 proof. Luke then burned brown sugar in a skillet, and mixed it in until the mixture had a mellow brown color.

"You see?" Luke told T. J. "We're giving the Indian a good product. Taste that. Don't that make you want to slap your Daddy on the back! They're going to love it! Nice and smooth, no headaches the next morning. But we got to have some strict rules, T. J. We'll probably have to give them a sample, but we can't have them drinking around the camp. We can't trade for horses; we're not in the horse business. Can't trade for squaws, either. All we want is buffalo robes. Good winter killed robes with prime fur."

The two of them mixed up a couple of barrels of liquor, then buried the rest of the grain alcohol back in the woods behind their camp. They could retrieve it when more was needed; now to get customers.

Luke saddled his riding horse a few days later and rode into Camp Robinson. He spent several days getting acquainted and met several men he knew, including some men who had been with Major Thornburgh the previous year. One day he ran into a Cheyenne-French half breed who had acted as a scout for the army while Luke was with Thornburgh. The breed was glad to see him, and was the go between Luke was looking for. He spoke fair English and remembered Luke killing the five Sioux the previous summer. Luke believed he could trust him as far as you could trust any breed in such a situation, and invited the man to visit their camp. The two rode back to Luke's hideaway.

Luke showed the breed their trading stock of pots and pans, skillets, as well as the bolts of cloth, needles and thread. Then the stock of coffee, sugar, cornmeal, flour, and the kegs of dried fruit. Finally, Luke brought out a jug of liquor and poured drinks for all three of them, then he watched the breed tip up his drink.

"It good!" The breed said, then asked, "You have more?"

Luke told him they did, but they wanted to trade for buffalo robes only and he added anyone who came to trade would have to take the liquor elsewhere to drink. He also impressed on him the need for secrecy, if the Indian Agent at Red Cloud, or the army learned they were here trading, they would soon be discovered and it would stop.

The breed nodded. "Sioux and Cheyenne very sad nowadays," he said. "No s'pose to hunt. Beef the agency give on the reservation is poor meat. Flour and cornmeal bad. Goddam, Injun need feel good! Injun like whiskey, too! I like your whiskey . . . is good. I bring you honest Injuns—no make trouble or try rob—just trade buffalo robes and have good time."

Luke poured the breed another drink and got up and began putting things into a sack. He measured out coffee, sugar, flour and cornmeal, then cut off several yards of calico cloth from a roll. He also gave the breed a pint of the liquor. "These presents I give to your wife," Luke said.

The breed put the sack across his horse's withers, shook hands with Luke and trotted off.

"I wonder if it'll work?" T. J. asked as the breed rode out of sight.

"I think so," Luke said. "The whites have taken their land,

and Ol' General Crook's army has starved them down, then disarmed them, and now the agency traders are short changing them with the rations they were promised. That breed is going back and tell them where they can trade buffalo robes for coffee and sugar and things for their squaws, and—"

"And whiskey!" T. J. said, grinning.

"And our specially made whiskey," Luke agreed. "Guess we ought to give it a brand name. He looked up at the top of the pines swaying in the breeze. "How's about calling it, Ol' Pine Top?"

"Sounds good to me," T. J. said.

* * *

The next day the breed returned with a dozen Indians. Half of them were Indian women and each led a pack horse loaded down with buffalo robes. Luke and T. J. spread their stock of trade goods on several blankets on the ground outside the tent, while Luke explained the exchange rates to the women. He planned on making a modest profit on the trade goods; it was the liquor where they would make the real money. "Let's call it a luxury tax," he'd told T. J. the day before. "If the bucks think the price too high—they don't have to trade, do they?"

The women picked up the pots and pans and skillets. They smelled the coffee beans and tasted the sugar by licking their fingers and sticking them into the five gallon sugar tins, and finally examined the bolts of cloth for color and feel. They again asked Luke the exchange rates, and seemed satisfied.

Soon they were unloading the robes from the horses. Luke went through the robes and graded them for quality. These northern robes were taken in late fall and winter and were much superior to the ones from Kansas and Texas. Also, no one could tan them better that these Indian women.

As soon as Luke had spotted the Indians coming, he had

told T. J. to make a big pot of coffee, while he had taken the two barking dogs back into the woods and tied them up. He had wanted the Indians to know they had guard dogs in camp. Now, he served coffee to the Indians and let them sweeten it with brown sugar.

The Indian men drank their coffee, but seemed more interested in the "whiskey". Any alcoholic drink was whiskey to them. They kept asking for a sample. Finally, Luke told the breed they could have one drink, then could trade one robe for one jug of liquor, but they must leave before opening the jug.

This was immediately agreed upon, with the Indians apparently thinking they had the best of the bargain.

When the trading was finished, the women loaded up their goods on the pack horses, and mounted up. The men followed with their whiskey jugs.

The breed stayed behind, knowing he would be favored with a few trade items and even perhaps a jug. Luke gave him his commission, and he seemed well satisfied. He then followed his Indian friends across the creek toward the Red Cloud Reservation.

* * *

The next weeks were busy ones for Luke and T. J. The robes poured in and as soon as they had a wagon load, T. J. drove it south to Sidney and shipped the robes to their dealer in Omaha. The dealer was so happy with the business, he became their agent as well, and began to order and ship their trading supplies to Sidney for T. J. to pick up. He meticulously sent them receipts for everything, and deposited their money in their bank account. All in all, the partners were pleased with the man they had picked to do business with.

The breed's French name was hard to pronounce, and Luke began calling him Charlie. Charlie soon saw that he had created a special spot for himself as a go between, and he played the position for all it was worth. Soon he had gone to the Spotted Tail Agency, and developed a large clientele.

Luke stayed busy, trading during the days, and often mixing up and bottling Ol' Pine Top at night.

Sometime in late November, Charlie the breed, came to him and told him that he'd heard several hardcase Indians at Spotted Tail were planning on raiding Luke's camp and killing him and taking his stock of trading supplies and liquor. T. J. was away hauling a load of robes to Sidney, and Luke was alone to figure out how he was going to handle the raid.

Luke knew quite a bit about how Indians operated; they would very likely try to take him in the early morning about daylight. He wouldn't have much warning. Very likely the dogs would be killed first, he knew. There was not really much he could do about it, but he would be alerted by them if he was on his toes, then it was up to him. He set about getting ready.

First, he dug a long, shallow hole just within a thicket perhaps forty yards from the trading tent. He chose a spot that gave him a good view, and lined the trench with pine branches, then buffalo robes. He bent pine limbs over the trench and camouflaged the hideout. Luke let one of the dogs loose, and kept the other tied up near the tent. When Charlie brought his Indian customers, Luke had always tied up both dogs behind the tent.

Luke slept in the camouflaged trench with his .44-40 Winchester carbine and a shotgun. One morning a couple of days after Charlie had warned him, he was awakened by a yip down by the creek, and knew that an Indian had killed the loose dog with an arrow. The dog that was tied up began to raise a racket, and soon there was the soft sound of a bowstring, and that dog died with a few whimpers. Luke listened to a crow overhead give its warning, then watched the area around the tent with his carbine ready.

It was perhaps twenty minutes before he saw the first Indian slip out of the woods behind the tent. Presently another joined him. From the direction of the creek came an Indian, then another from across the open space to the west. The two Indians which had come out of the woods behind, silently slipped up to the rear of the tent, and Luke knew that they would slit the canvas and try to kill him in his sleep. Presently the Indians came out the front opening and motioned to the other two. They all converged, and seemed to be talking it over, wondering where he had gone.

It seemed to be as good as time as any, and Luke eared back the hammer on the carbine. His sights found two of the Indians overlapping, and he shot and knocked them down. He jacked another cartridge into the chamber, and caught another Indian running, and put him down. The fourth had almost made it to the timber, when Luke shot him. It looked like three were down, and one wounded from that first shot. He was crawling away toward the thicket on the far side of the opening. Luke shot at him twice more, but the Indian got into the woods.

Luke reloaded, and waited. Several times he heard a sound like groan or a cough from one of the Indians that were down in front of the tent, but he could see no movement. The crows were now telling everyone about it, and the early morning breeze sighed through the tree tops. The first rays of the sun began to color the land, and the mountains stood out bold and clear beyond the camp. Luke waited, and felt sad, thinking of the dogs that had warned him. He knew that without them, he would never have had a chance.

Time dragged on and Luke wondered if there were more Indians waiting out there somewhere, waiting just as he was. He desperately wanted a smoke, and a cup of coffee. He watched as the sun rose above the trees and began to illuminate the opening in front of the tent. The bodies of the three Indians lay still.

He lay there until the sun was high above, then finally slipped out and skirted the timber as he worked around toward where the wounded had Indian crawled. Luke took his time; no use getting in a hurry now, he told himself. An hour later he picked up blood sign, and took his time as he followed it. Now was not the time to be caught unaware.

Finally he found the Indian. He had been hit several times and was dead.

Back at his camp he checked the three Indians and made sure they were dead. He lit a smoke, and built a fire in the rock fireplace. Then he put water and coffee into the coffee pot, set it over the fire, and went back to look at the dog that had been tied up; it had an arrow through its chest, and was dead. He walked back into the trees and made his way to the creek. Soon he found the other dog, also dead with an arrow through it. Beyond the creek perhaps a quarter of a mile, he picked up sign of their horses, and soon found four Indian ponies tied up. He scouted the area and could not find any more sign; finally he took off the Indian bridles and turned the ponies loose.

Back at his camp, Luke poured coffee, and tried to calm his pounding heart. As he stood there sipping the scalding coffee, he decided there was no greater feeling than combat when you put everything on the line—and won out. It was almost like putting everything you owned on one card at the faro table, then waited to see that turn of the second card. But if you lost in faro, you continued to live, and could start all over.

That afternoon Luke was busy as he dug a big grave out

behind the tent and buried the four Indians.[1]

The following day, T. J. showed up, and they broke camp and moved to another site a few miles away. Luke sure didn't want to be caught with four dead Sioux behind his camp. Business continued to be good, and on his next trip to Sidney, T. J. stopped by the old dog man and bought two more dogs. Sometime late in January, they were caught in a terrible blizzard, and business slowed to practically nothing. The partners decided to call it a season, buried their barrels of alcohol, packed up, and drove south.

They left their wagons, trading goods, and horses and dogs with the dog man, and paid him to care for them until they returned the next summer.

They stayed in Sidney for several days at the Moore Hotel and ate in the restaurant next door. On the first day Luke and T. J. bought new clothing from Oberfelder's Clothing Store, took long baths, and got dressed in their new duds. It was a great feeling to finally unwind. They drank at several of the saloons. Luke met Sam Bass, a man soon to be a noted stagecoach, train, and bank robber, who would have a ballad written about him. Bass was also a Texan, and Luke and T. J. liked him right off. Bass was killed in Texas after trying to rob a Round Rock bank not long afterward.

At this time Sidney was about the roughest town in the west, with many of the toughest elements from Texas. One of these men was a Texan named James Riley. Riley had gotten into trouble in Texas, and escaped from a jail. He had come to Nebraska and taken the name of Doc Middleton. On the night of January 14, 1877, a Sunday, Luke and T. J. were in Joe Lane's Dance Hall when trouble broke out. There were two bars on the ground floor of Lane's establishment, and upstairs were rooms where the girl's entertained. Sundays were designated to be "Soldiers Night," and only soldiers from the nearby Sidney Barracks were allowed to go upstairs with the girls. Luke and T. J. were drinking at one of the bars when Doc Middleton and several other cowboys came in.

There were also a few bullwhackers in the bars, and all seemed to know one another. The girls on the ground floor were friendly to all, but were not supposed to go upstairs with anyone but soldiers on Sunday. One of the girls apparently liked Doc Middleton, and was talking to him, when one of the soldiers made a nasty remark to Middleton. A fight was imminent, the soldiers on one side, and cowboys and teamsters on the other.

One of the soldiers knocked Middleton down, and a free-for-all started. Luke and T. J. got back out of the way, and were enjoying the fight, when the lights went out. Middleton used the darkness to draw his pistol, and shot the soldier in the chest. He died instantly.

At the sound of the shot, the soldiers broke off and ran back to the fort for their weapons. The town marshal, unaware that someone had been killed, helped Middleton escape before the soldiers returned with their rifles. Luke and T. J. got out of there, and watched the soldiers bombard the saloon and dance hall from the front of the Moore Hotel.

The marshal and a Lt. Hammond finally got the soldiers to stop shooting up the place, but Doc Middleton was long gone. Middleton afterwards got into stealing horses from not only ranchers, but also began raiding the Red Cloud and Spotted Tail Agencies and stealing Indian ponies. Robbery and murder came next, and eventually he was caught and put back into prison.

Luke and T. J. got on the eastbound train the next day and rode to Omaha. Here they met with their agent, and settled up for the season. The man told them he had developed a good market back east, and there was a great demand for the robes. He said that he might be able to pay them a dollar or two more per robe the next season.

They said goodby, and rode on to Kansas City where Luke had stored his things. After a few days, T. J. said goodby, and went on to St. Louis and took a steamboat south to Texas.

Luke spent the rest of the winter there in Kansas City. He made the Marble Hall his headquarters, and even dealt cards for Joe Bassett. He was in contact with Chalk Beeson and Bill Harris, and just before the cattle season began in late May, he went back to Dodge.

CHAPTER TWELVE

In Dodge City Luke Short found that Chalk Beeson and Bill Harris had bought the Long Branch Saloon from Robert Wright. The Long Branch was located on Front Street, near the corner of Second Avenue. Directly on the corner was the two story building of Wright's large store. Between Wright's store and the Long Branch was a narrow building that housed the Alamo Saloon. To the right of the Long Branch was Hoover's Wholesale Liquors and Saloon. The Long Branch was perhaps thirty feet wide, and a hundred feet long. Beeson and Harris had just finished decorating it, as they waited for the first Texas trail herds to show from the south. The bar was in the front part, of course, to the right of the entrance, and naturally, it had a large pair of longhorns mounted above the back bar mirror. There were tables farther back for drinking and gambling. Beyond were two additional rooms. One contained a billiard table, the other one had poker tables where serious players could concentrate without interruptions. Large pictures in fancy frames were along the walls.

Chalk Beeson had imported a five piece orchestra from Kansas City to draw in the cowboys when they came. Beeson was also a talented violinist himself, and often played with the group. No dancing was allowed in the Long Branch, but you could drink and gamble to your heart's content, and listen to the music every night.

Luke settled in at his favorite corner room at the Western House with Dr. Galland and his wife. Luke always brought presents to the people he liked, and had bought a stylish Sunday hat for Mrs. Galland. He also had a book of poetry for the Doctor.

Beeson and Harris had been impressed with the job Luke had done the previous year at the Saratoga, and now put him in charge of the gambling operation. With Luke back to run the games and draw in his Texas friends, together with the new band Beeson had imported, the partners looked forward to an even bigger season than the previous one.

Luke was delighted to again see his friends, Bat and Ed Masterson, and Wyatt Earp, when he arrived in May. Wyatt was soon hired as Assistant Marshal. Luke also got to know Doc Holliday. Much has been said of Holliday and his orneriness; there is no doubt Doc could get ornery, particularly when he was drinking, which was most of the time. Bat Masterson has said in almost all his accounts he didn't like Holliday but put up with him because Holliday and Wyatt Earp were close. Doc either liked you or he didn't. Doc and Luke respected one another and got along fine. Both were Southerners; their sympathies would forever be with the Confederacy, and they would always detest the carpetbaggers who had taken over their country after the Civil War. Doc had just come to Dodge from Fort Griffin in Texas where he had knifed a man named Bailey in an altercation over a card game. Doc was in the right, and only cut Bailey after he began to draw his six-shooter. He had submitted to arrest, but many of Bailey's friends began talking of lynching Doc. Big Nosed Kate Fisher, a dance hall girl, had started a fire to distract the members of the hanging party. She then slipped Doc a revolver, and the two rode out of Fort Griffin and came to Dodge. Doc was at this time trying to stay out of trouble, and even hung up his dentist shingle. In fact, this was when

Luke really got to know him when he went to have Doc take care of an aching tooth

As sheriff of Ford County, Bat was busy that year of 1878. In January Bat had headed a posse that trailed two robbers sixty-five miles south of Dodge and captured them; two more of the gang were arrested in the town.

In April, at the elections, the Gang was reinstated; Dog Kelley as mayor, and others of the businessmen who believed in a free and open town were elected to the City Council.

Just a week after that election, the popular marshal, Ed Masterson was shot and killed. Jack Wagner and several cowboys who had just come to Dodge, were drinking and dancing in the Lady Gay Saloon and Dance Hall south of the tracks. With Wagner was Alf Walker, the trail boss for cattleman Oburn of Kansas City. The party became louder and wilder, and because the cowboys were carrying pistols in violation of the city's ordinances, Marshal Masterson and one of his policeman, a man named Nat Haywood, were called. Masterson soon disarmed the drunken Wagner, who was wearing a six-shooter in a shoulder holster. The dancing and drinking resumed, and not thinking there would be trouble, Masterson and Haywood stepped outside onto the boardwalk. As they stood there, the drunken Wagner somehow got hold of a pistol, and ran outside. Masterson grabbed the armed man, not wanting to shoot him. As Haywood went to help his boss, two of Wagner's friends drew hidden pistols, and one stuck his in Haywood's face and pulled the trigger. The cap snapped, but the charge didn't fire. At the same time, Wagner shot Marshal Masterson in the stomach. He was so close Masterson's shirt caught fire. Ed Masterson, mortally wounded, pulled his six-shooter, and shot several times. One shot hit Wagner in the belly, others hit the cowboys' trail boss, Alf Walker, who had drawn a pistol and come to Wagner's aid. It happened so fast, that later no one could be certain just who had fired, but Walker was hit in the lung and two other shots broke his arm.

Wagner staggered into Peacock's saloon where he collapsed. Masterson, with a gaping hole in his abdomen, staggered across the railroad tracks, and 450 feet to George Hoover's liquor store. He fell to the floor, and was carried to his brother's room and put upon the bed. Bat and Ed's friends stayed with him, but they held no hope. Ed Masterson died about forty minutes after being shot.

Wagner and Walker, were carried to a room above Wright's store. Wagner died the next day, but Walker would recover.

Although Bat arrested several more of the cowboys who had been involved in the fight, none of them were charged. The shooting had taken place outside the dance hall in the dark, and was over before any reliable witnesses had seen it. They were turned loose and soon went back to Texas.

Around ten o'clock, on the day following Ed Masterson's death, all the businesses closed, and many of them were draped with crepe. Ed did not have the flamboyant manner of Bat, but he was mourned by most everyone, for he had been a superb peace officer, always reluctant to use his pistol, if it could be avoided. This time, he had waited too long.

Services were held in Dodge, and Rev. O. W. Wright gave the sermon. Mr. and Mrs. Chalk Beeson sang: "*Lay him low, lay him low. In the clover or the snow—What cares he, he cannot know.*"[1]

Luke hired a buggy from Ham Bell's Livery, and drove Mr. and Mrs. Galland as the funeral procession slowly followed the hearse five miles east to the military cemetery at Fort Dodge, where he was buried. There were many wet eyes when Ed was put beneath the sod.

Soon afterward, Bat Masterson made the trip to the home of his parents in Sedwick, Kansas, to tell them the sad news of Ed's death.

Charlie Bassett was promoted to take Ed Masterson's place as marshal of Dodge, and Jim Masterson was hired as Deputy Marshal around the first of June.

About 265,000 Texas longhorns were driven north to Dodge that season, and there were 1,300 to 1,500 cowboys to drive them. As soon as the cowboys were paid off, they proceeded to get rid of their money. Everyone in the business got a share, the stores and boot shops, the saddlery, the saloon and gambling and dance halls, and the painted women who came from Kansas City and St. Louis.

Besides Luke Short there was an impressive list of professional gamblers, men like Colonel Charlie Norton, Joe Mason, Charlie Bassett, Lou and Sam Blonger, Harry Bell, Cockeyed Frank Loving, Mysterious Dave Mather, Shotgun Collins, Rowdy Joe Lowe, Luke's old idol, Dick Clark from Abilene, and many others. Wyatt and his two brothers, Virgil and Morgan, also pinch-hit as gamblers, as did the deadly dentist, Doc Holliday. Doc soon pulled down his shingle; it was a lot more fun drinking and gambling than looking in someone's dirty mouth, anyway.

The *Globe* announced in June: "Three dancehalls in full blast on the southside, stables jammed full, hundreds of cowboys perambulate daily, but two cases in police court. Who says we aren't a moral city?"

In July, Deputy United States Marshal H. T. McCarty was killed as he stood at the Long Branch's bar talking to friends. A drunken, dimwitted cook from one of the cow camps had pulled McCarty's pistol from his holster, and killed him with it.

Eddie Foy, the celebrated vaudeville performer, and his partner, Jim Thompson, performed at the Comique, and were a great hit with the cowboys and townspeople, alike. Ham Bell opened the Varieties, a rival theater, and soon had Dora Hand on the stage. Dora was billed as the Queen of the Fairy

Belles. She was a beautiful woman, who captured the cowboys' hearts, and yet, was respected by the businessmen's wives with whom she sang in the church choir on Sundays. Dora was killed later in the fall after Luke left for Nebraska. She had been sleeping in Dog Kelley's bed while Kelly was away, sick in the Fort Dodge Hospital. A drunken cowboy, who had fought with Kelley, shot through the thin walls and killed her, thinking he had gotten the Mayor. Her unknowing slayer was James Kenedy, who was the son of Captain Miflin Kenedy, the wealthy cattle baron from down on the Texas gulf.

Sheriff Bat Masterson, Assistant Marshal Wyatt Earp, Marshal Charlie Bassett, Deputy Sheriff Bill Duffy, and Bill Tilghman went after the cowboy. The posse thought Kenedy would head straight for home, and rode hard to cut him off. They got ahead of him, then turned back and caught him as he approached a ranch near Meade.

Masterson ordered Kenedy to throw up his hands, and when he did not, and looked like he was pulling his rifle, several shots rang out as the posse fired. Probably any of the men would have killed him outright, after his cowardly shooting of Dora. Kenedy was hit in the shoulder and knocked from his saddle. Three other shots killed his horse.

When Masterson approached him with six-shooter in hand, young Kenedy asked, "Did I get that bastard Kelly?"

"No, you cowardly son-of-a-bitch!" Bat said. "You killed Dora Hand, who was sleeping in Dog Kelly's bed."

Masterson later, in telling Luke about it, said the cowboy began to cry.

Kenedy's arm was shattered, and several pieces of bone were removed. In December the senior Kenedy arrived with his personal doctor to oversee his medical treatment, and to hire lawyers for his defense. Though everyone knew that young Kenedy had fired the shots which killed Dora, no one had actually seen him shoot. With Miflin Kenedy's lawyers working, he was soon released and went home with his father. Even with a crippled arm he managed to kill a couple of other men while drinking, but in a little more than a year he met a man who was a little faster, and sent him to the place he so justly deserved.

In September Luke received a letter from T. J. in Omaha, saying that he had ordered their trading supplies, and was proceeding on to Sidney to get the wagons and teams ready for their fall trading venture. He asked Luke to try and get away from Dodge as soon as he could.

The cattle season was starting to wind down and Luke had already talked to Bill Harris about leaving early. Harris was a professional gambler himself, and told Luke he would take over the management of the gambling hall if he wanted to go.

Just as Luke was packing, word came that Dull Knife and Little Wolf, Northern Cheyenne chiefs, had broken out of their reservation in Indian Territory, and with about 300 followers, were headed north toward their hunting grounds in the Big Horn Country. Dull Knife had surrendered back in the winter of 1876-77 when he had been surprised by Colonel Ranald S. McKenzie on the Red Forks of the Powder River.

Box Eldor, an old, blind medicine man, had predicted the white men were coming before McKenzie's attack, but here it was in the middle of the winter, and the Cheyennes were comfortable in their winter camp. Many of them couldn't believe that the cavalry would be out looking for them in that kind of weather. There was practically no one in the camp of Indians who believed the old man, and many thought he was absolutely crazy. In any event, McKenzie was near, and did attack. In addition to his army, he had 400 scouts, some of them Pawnee and Shoshone, but also many Cheyenne and Sioux who had quit fighting the whites, and enlisted to fight their own people. Dull Knife wasn't expecting these turncoats. McKenzie's cavalry charged into the Cheyenne village, and killed and drove the hostiles out into the bitter weather. McKenzie let his Indian scouts take what they wanted from the winter lodges, then burned the rest, clothing and bedding and stored food. He also took 600 of the Cheyennes' horse herd. The homeless Cheyenne survivors watched all this from a nearby mountain, then began the long walk along the slope of the Big Horn, then down the Powder, and across the Tongue until they came to Crazy Horse's camp. The Oglalas took them in and fed them, but they had problems of their own, and let the Cheyennes know that they couldn't stay long.

Finally, it was clear to Dull Knife they would have to surrender, for the old people and children were starving and freezing to death.

When they did do so, they were disarmed and sent to Oklahoma Territory, a place that they hated, for they were mountain people.

Now, on September 8, 1878, after almost two years in the hated Oklahoma Territory, they'd had enough, and Dull Knife and Little Wolf gathered their people, the few rifles they had acquired, their horses, and broke out, 300 of them, willing to die if they had to, in order to get back home.

Unconfirmed reports trickled into Dodge every day, and the old Indian fighters thought that they would likely pass close to Dodge City. On September 16, a war party struck at Meade City on Crooked Creek, south of Dodge. A mail carrier was killed and his horse and weapons and clothing taken. Another band ransacked the Champman and Tuttle ranch. There were only nineteen soldiers stationed at Fort Dodge, and now all the local residents were worried. A company of volunteers was organized, and cavalry was ordered out into the field from Fort Leavenworth.

Luke Short had already taken the train to Omaha, then

Sidney, to meet with T. J. He did not know that the desperate Cheyennes would raid and kill and secure more weapons and horses, and defeat several armies as they fought their way toward their homeland, nor did he realize that his old friend Major Thomas Thornburgh would again tap him as a dispatch rider and scout.

CHAPTER THIRTEEN

Luke rented a horse at the livery stable and rode north of town to the dog man's cabin. T. J. was delighted to see him, and was full of news. He told Luke that he and the old man had repaired all the harnesses and taken the wheels from the wagons and checked and greased everything. The country was in an uproar over Dull Knife and Little Wolf's rampage through Kansas.

The old man also seemed glad to see him, and pumped his arm delightedly. It seemed very likely the old man sensed what kind of business they were engaged in, and was supportive of them. He had been well paid for keeping their wagons, and caring for their horses all the time they had been gone, and finally T. J. suggested they hire him to help them set up their new camp north of the Indian Agencies. "He speaks Sioux and some Cheyenne, and knows signs," T. J. said, "he'd be a lot of help."

"If you think so," Luke said, and when they broached the subject, the old man was delighted.

"I may be old," he said, "but I can help you a lot."

"It might get pretty hairy this season, Dad," Luke said.

The old man just grinned at him, and said, "I'm seventy-four, and I fought Injuns most of my life." He lifted his battered hat to show his bald head, "what they gonna do, take my hair?"

"What about your place here?"

"My tame Injuns will watch it. We'll take two of my best dogs, and I'll get a neighbor to take the others until I get back."

They left the next day, as soon as the old man had taken his dogs to the neighbor's ranch. They drove into Sidney to the train depot and loaded the trading stock T. J. had bought in Omaha.

It took them a full week to get beyond Camp Robinson. Again they picked a site with a view of the approach of anyone coming toward their camp, a place in the trees near a good stream.

They had brought some lumber this time, and built a real tent frame, then erected the much larger tent that T. J. had bought in Omaha. When completed, the three of them moved all their trading stock inside, except for two barrels of grain alcohol. The rest of the barrels they buried out in the woods behind the tent.

The following day they hauled water from the creek and began mixing the liquor. The old man worked at filling the pint jugs and kegs with a funnel. The previous year the partners had realized they could also use larger containers for their special blend of Ol' Pine Top, so in Omaha, T. J. had ordered more small kegs of two-and-a-half, and five gallon sizes. Luke had come up with the idea of a bunch of Indians going together and trading for enough liquor for a party. What they'd do, Luke told T. J., was to bury some of these kegs perhaps ten miles away, and tell the Indians where they were located after they traded.

The old man had to sample their product to see if it was fit to drink, and soon had a grin on his face. "I'll say this for you boys, you sure turn out a real smooth product!"

"Well, I don't believe in mixing up that rotgut like the others do," Luke said, "putting in tobacco and pepper and all that other stuff to give it a bite."

"I'll drink to that!" The old man said.

Soon they made contact with the breed, Charlie. He was happy to see them back, but warned that several other bootleggers were operating in the area. Some of them were tough hombres, and he cautioned Luke and T. J. to keep a sharp watch out for them.

Luke and T. J. knew it wasn't going to be as easy as the previous year, and he and T. J. devised an escape plan. Luke had been leery of Omaha as a place to keep the money they made, since it was where the Department of the Platte Army Headquarters was located. Also, if one or both of them were caught, that was where they would be taken and held for trial.

Luke told T. J. that on his first trip south with a load of buffalo robes to take the train to Denver and open accounts in both of their names at a bank. Then he should go east and make an arrangement with their dealer-agent in Omaha to deduct the amount of the supplies he bought for them, and send the rest of the money to Denver to be deposited to their accounts.

It was a good thing this was soon accomplished, for trouble was on their horizon.

The buffalo robes had begun to roll in again. Soon there were perhaps as many as 6,000 Indians on the two agencies, and there was a report that a new one would soon be started northwest of them in Dakota Territory, to be called Pine Ridge. Luke wanted to get all the robes they could before some of the Indians would be moved there. Robes seemed plentiful, some families had many of them. Most of the Indians had hidden rifles before coming to the agencies, and now and then would slip off and go hunting back in their old grounds. These men brought buffalo hides back for their wives to tan. Also, many of these Indians sometimes raided the Crows and Shoshones and brought back horses, hides and other furs.

The small kegs of liquor worked out well. A group of Indians would bring enough robes to trade for a keg of liquor, and Luke would draw them a map of where the keg was hidden, together with land marks or blazes on trees. The Indians had been leery of being cheated, at first, but soon came to trust him. This way the robes piled up faster, and the drunks were farther away.

But things were happening all around, and Luke knew it was just a matter of time before they were ambushed by some of their competition, or the army would find them out. Something told him to pull up and go now, but the robes kept coming in great number, and T. J. and the old man were busy hauling loads of robes to Sidney to ship to Omaha. In fact, it seemed the two men were on the road most of the time.

T. J. was bringing back news of Dull Knife's breakout. It seemed the telegraph was kept busy with the reports. Many people were wondering what the army was doing, if anything. Former Indian fighters claimed that the only way to catch the renegades was to put soldiers ahead of them in such numbers as to make it impossible for them to continue on. This was done but the ragtag Indian band had broken through the army troops near Dodge City, then another army south of the Kansas Pacific tracks in a canyon near Famished Woman Creek. Neither battle stopped the Indians, and people around North Platte, Ogallala and Sidney, Nebraska were becoming alarmed. Down on the Sappa in northern Kansas, the Indians raided farms and ranches as they swept north gathering more weapons and horses as they progressed. George Rowley was returning from Ogallala to his ranch on Stinking Water Creek, and Dull Knife's warriors killed him and took his outfit. The Indians killed anyone in their path, and kept riding north. People began to fort up in their homes, waiting.

When T. J. and the old man returned from a trip, Luke

already had another wagon load of robes ready to go, and he decided to drive that load to Sidney himself, and take a much needed break. He left T. J. to run the trading post, and he and the old man headed south.

There was one thing that both T. J. and Luke agreed on, with the army going wild and running across the country chasing Indians, they wouldn't have to worry about soldiers looking for them.

Luke and the old man got unloaded in Sidney and shipped the robes to their dealer in Omaha, then picked up their freight and made ready to leave town. As the old man drove back down the main street, Luke stopped at a saloon to have a drink and pick up news of the renegade Indians. A soldier Luke knew saw him, and soon Major Thomas Thornburgh, his old commander, sent word asking Luke to come to his office at the barracks.

Thornburgh had been put in command of all troops along the railroad line which followed the curve of the Platte. The Major told him he desperately needed men as dispatch riders and scouts, and finally persuaded Luke to sign on as a dispatch rider until the principal Indian leaders, Dull Knife, Little Wolf, Wild Hog, Old Crow, Left Hand, Porcupine, and Nosey Walker were either killed or captured. Luke privately thought taking the job might ally any suspicions that might be floating around Camp Robinson about what he did for a living, and on that day, October 6, 1878, he signed on with the army again as a dispatch rider for the sum of ten dollars a day.[1]

Luke immediately rode out of town and caught up with the old man. He told him to tell T. J. what he had done, and why. Luke also told the old man that the two of them should stay at their camp and continue trading for buffalo robes until they saw or heard from him again. He turned then, and rode back to Sidney Barrack.

There he drew a big, strong army horse from the stable, and left his own in the army corral. He drew ammunition for his six-shooter, and for the .44-40 carbine, then collected his bedroll and warbag, and reported to Thornburgh.

Thornburgh soon had a report that the hostiles had crossed the rail lines a mere mile east of Ogallala, as if showing their contempt for the pony soldiers who had tried to stop them all across Kansas. Thornburgh immediately loaded his command, horses, and supplies aboard the train and raced east to intercept the renegades. Luke went along with the Major's command. As soon as Thornburgh's command was unloaded at Ogallala, they took to the field, and soon picked up the Indians' trail. Luke, always a first class trailer, was soon riding ahead with the other scouts, until he was called upon to carry a dispatch.

Several days later, as they were closing on the rear of Dull Knife's band, the Indians began to split up into groups and scatter, typical Indian procedure. The trails led unerringly northwest into the sand hills between the Platte and the Niobrara Rivers. Major Thornburgh finally decided to stop; there was in those days talk that the blowing sand and the dunes could bog down men and horses, and he worried his command might get separated and lost. Thornburgh sent Luke back to the road with a dispatch for the commanding officer at Camp Robinson, telling the direction the hostiles were heading.

There was little danger of the hostile Cheyennes coming back that way. They were desperate to get back to their own country in the Big Horn Mountains.

Near the last days in October, Thornburgh's command was back at Sidney Barracks. Luke received his pay, then turned in his army horse, and claimed his own. He shook hands with the Major, then rode out of town, and headed north. It was to be the last time he would work for the army.

Dull Knife and Little Wolf differed on tactics and each leader took his followers and went his own way. Both bands finally were again forced to give up as the winter worsened. They had broken out of their reservation in Oklahoma because of the fever that was killing them, then fought a desperate battle across three states, living off the land while outmarching fresh army troops, and outfighting three military departments.

Luke had feared and fought Indians as a boy in Texas and his feelings were probably much like any other frontiersman, but he must have admired what this ragged band of Indians had accomplished. Beyond the fighting, they had also moved their sick and wounded, the small children, and the old men and women of their tribe with them on their desperate flight to return to their homeland.

The sand hills which had stopped Thornburgh's pursuit of Dull Knife's band would, in ten years, become some of the best ranching country in Nebraska.

Luke would soon see his friend, the Major, one more time, but it would be under different circumstances. Luke would be in the guardhouse at Sidney Barracks.

CHAPTER FOURTEEN

After Luke returned from chasing Dull Knife and his band with Thornburgh, things seemed to return to normal, but a few weeks later he was in a deadly gunfight. He was alone at the camp when his Indian dogs alerted him to visitors. Two men had left their horses hidden in the timber across the creek, and approached on foot. They hallooed the camp, and Luke quieted the dogs, then stepped out to meet them. There were two tough looking white men, one carrying a Winchester carbine and wearing a six-shooter, one with two revolvers around his waist.

"We got a camp over to the east about ten miles," one of the men said, "and was wondering if you got any liquor to sell?"

As the man spoke, his partner was moving slowly off to one side. From the looks of them Luke thought they were some of his competitors, and one of his Indian customers had told them where he was located, probably in return for a jug of liquor. They no doubt had been watching the camp and saw that he was alone. The two weren't interested in buying liquor; they intended on killing him, and taking everything.

"No," Luke said, watching the man on his left with the rifle.

The rifle began to come up, and Luke drew and hammered two quick shots into the man, then whirled as the other began to shoot. A burning sensation hit him in the side, but by then he was lined up on the man with two guns. Luke's first shot was good, but he shot the man twice more as he fell. Then he ducked into the doorway of the tent and grabbed a loaded double-barreled shotgun, and covered the two downed men. The first man was moving on the ground and crying out, but it was all over.

Luke walked over and took their weapons, and stood there for several minutes looking at the dying man, watching for any movement on the other side of the creek. He saw nothing, and reloaded his six-shooter. The dogs were raising a racket, and he quieted them down. He then went inside and examined his wound. The bullet had cut a deep groove along the right side of his chest, exposing the white of a rib bone. It would be painful for awhile, but didn't amount to much. He mixed up a little coal oil with lard and brown sugar, and covered the wound, winding around it a long strip of cloth from one of the bolts of material that he used to trade with the Indian women.

When he finished, he checked both men out front. They were dead. Luke traded the shotgun for his .44-40 carbine, then tied up one of the dogs. Taking the other one, he crossed the creek and began his scout. Presently the dog began snarling, and Luke watched cautiously as it nosed a spot overlooking the creek, and their camp beyond. Luke knelt and saw where someone had been lying. Shortly he found moccasin prints. Luke followed the dog across a low ridge, and saw two horses tied to branches. The dog went to a third spot, and Luke found where the Indian's unshod horse had stood. He scouted the area, but found no more sign, Then mounting one of the horses, he led the other and crossed the creek.

At the camp, Luke put the rifle of the one gunmen back into it's scabbard beneath the saddle skirt, and hung their gunbelts around their saddle horns. He stood there for a long time thinking of what to do. With the Army on the lookout for bootleggers, it sure wouldn't be good if they found these two men buried back in the woods behind the camp. It would be a murder charge, but if there were no bodies, there would only be a charge of selling liquor to the Indians. So he must take the bodies where they wouldn't be found.

Luke hoisted the men's bodies across their horses' saddles, and lashed them there, then he saddled his own horse and found a shovel. He led the two horses back behind the camp along an old deer trail and into broken country that he had been over before. Several miles farther he came to a place where the land was split with fissures. He found a good spot, untied the two dead men and dumped them into a deep crack. He then took their weapons and the saddles and bridles from their horses and turned them loose. Luke threw the weapons and bridles and saddles in on top of the men, shoveled dirt over them, then rolled rocks into the fissure. It was unlikely that they would ever be found, but if they were, he planned to be long gone.[1]

He rode back to his camp and, breaking one of his rules, poured himself a tin cup of his Ol' Pine Top, and began to check his wound. The two dogs came into the tent and lay down, watching him. "You boys did real good," he said and petted them.

When T. J. and Dog Man returned from Sidney he told them of the gunfight, and what he had done with their competitors' bodies. "I couldn't see moving the camp again,"

Luke said, "so I just moved them. You can't stay hidden in this business, anyway."

"No," T. J. said. "Dad, here, picked up a little news from a breed at Spotted Tail. Tell him, Dad."

"Well, it sounds like the Army has orders to clear out all the bootleggers around the country, alright. They're offering rewards for information."

"Ah," Luke said, "Indeed!"

That evening after supper, Luke and T. J. walked together down along the creek, with the two Indians dogs running ahead, doing the thing they had been trained to do, sniff out Indians.

"We've had a good running hand, here, but I think we better get out, don't you?" Luke asked.

"Yeah. The sooner the better."

"I've got a fair load of robes for you, T. J.," Luke said, "let's go back and load them up tonight, and you and the old man can leave the first thing in the morning."

"Then what?"

"You go on into Sidney and ship the robes to Omaha, then sell the team and wagon and go to the old man's place and wait for me. I'll tell Charlie we're shutting down, then I'll bury the rest of the alcohol, load up the other trade goods, and head for Sidney, too. We'll peddle what's left—and *vamos!*"

Luke whistled for the dogs, and they turned back. "One other thing, T. J., if I was to get caught, you don't know me. Take off! It will only be a charge of selling liquor to Indians, and I don't really know what they'd do. Maybe they'll just kick me out of the country."

T. J. looked at him seriously. "Well, I'll see you in Sidney, then, and if not there, in Denver."

Luke nodded. "You haven't told the old man anything

about Denver, have you?"

T. J. shook his head.

"Good."

T. J. and the old man left early the next morning.

That afternoon, Charlie, the breed, brought several customers to trade. There was something about Charlie that bothered Luke, but he couldn't figure out what it was. Maybe he was just getting jumpy. After they were gone, he went out and closely checked the places when the would-be killers had died. He had covered the bloody spots with dirt and made it look natural, but now he wondered if Charlie had somehow spotted them. Charlie could follow sign with the best of them, and was hard to beat as a trailer. Probably he was just getting nervous, he decided.

Late that evening he loaded the remaining wagon with the robes he had just acquired, then carried the rest of his trading stock, the pots and pans and skillets, the bolts of cloth, and the food stuff out and stowed them away. He rolled the remaining barrels liquor out in the back, and buried them, planning on an early start the next morning.

The next morning he brought in the team before it was even light, and was harnessing them when the dogs alerted him. Luke immediately went to the tent, and put a cartridge into the chamber of the .44-40. He stepped outside and moved to the trees. He didn't hear anything for some time, then came the sound of horses and the squeak of saddle leather. Presently he heard horses crossing the creek. Many of them. Then he began to see their shadowy forms.

Behind him in the woods came the sound of many men moving. Indians didn't make noise like that. It was the army.

Luke walked back to the tent, and leaned his rifle against the tent frame. He stood there, and the forms turned into cavalrymen riding up the slope toward him.

The officer, held up a gauntleted hand, and stopped the riders behind him. He was an officer Luke knew from the campaign of two years before. "Got any coffee left, Luke?" the officer asked, and began to swing down.

"I just put everything away," Luke said, "I'm breaking up camp, sorry."

The officer nodded to his men, and they dismounted. Other men on foot began to come out of the woods behind the tent.

"First off, let me have your revolver," the officer said.

Luke unbuckled his holster and cartridge belt and handed it to the officer.

"Maybe we could have a drink of Ol' Pine Top," the officer said with a grin, "there's a bit of a chill in the air."

"Well, I'd sure like to oblige," Luke said, "but I'm fresh out."

The officer picked up Luke's carbine, and handed it to a soldier, then stepped into the empty tent. When he came out a sergeant stepped up and reported: "Nothing in the wagon but trading supplies, sir, and maybe two dozen buffalo robes."

"Get a work party and start digging around back there in the woods," the officer said, pointing behind the tent.

It wasn't long before the sergeant come back with a grin, behind him were two men rolling a keg. They upended it in front of the tent, and the sergeant borrowed a rifle and used the butt to cave in the head. He knelt and sniffed the contents, then grinned. "We might have to sample the stuff, sir, to have a case."

"Of course."

The sergeant called for a tin cup, and dipped it in. He offered it to the officer, who took the cup and drank. After a moment, he said, "Ah, we've tasted some real rotgut this past

113

week, but boys, this is pretty good stuff! Sergeant, tell the men that they can fill their canteens."

"Yes, sir!"

"Luke, I hate to do this to an old campaigner—but you're under arrest," the officer said.

The sergeant produced handcuffs, and soon had them around Luke's wrists.

Meanwhile more liquor barrels were unearthed and rolled around to the front of the tent.

"Oh my, yes!" Said the officer. "Quite a little operation. All right, sergeant, when the men all have their canteens filled, leave one keg for the scout, then smash the rest and pour it out onto the ground. Put Mr. Short onto one of his horses, and chain his feet together, then you can take off the cuffs."

"What about my dogs?" Luke asked.

"We'll take them to Camp Robinson, and give them to someone. You won't be needing them where you're going!"

As they formed up to move out, Luke looked back and saw the breed, Charlie, standing beside the tent. Of course! Charlie would end up with the tent, his team and wagon and all that was in it. And being a good sign man, he would undoubtedly find several more kegs of uncut grain alcohol back in the woods.

They took Luke to Camp Robinson and kept him in the guardhouse overnight. The next morning a detail formed up and, with his feet again chained together beneath his mount, the sergeant and his men escorted him south to Sidney. Luke was again held in the guardhouse, and it was here that Major Thornburgh came to see him.

Luke could see the Major was genuinely sorry to see him in this position. "Jesus, I'm sorry about this, Luke!" He said.

114

"But it's out of my hands; the commanding officer at Robinson is the one preferring changes."

"Don't feel bad, Major—it's just the way the cards fell," Luke said, "I knew what I was doing when I got into it."

Thornburgh shook his head, then said, "When you get to Omaha, and your case comes up, write me and I'll send a letter of recommendation about your service with me. Maybe it will help a little."

"It's been good knowing you, Major," Luke said, and they shook hands.

* * *

Luke wouldn't see the gallant Major again. He was killed the following year in the Ute uprising over on the Milk River. Killed because of the idiocy of an Indian agent named Meeker.

The next morning Luke was marched to the station for the eastbound train. He wore handcuffs, and saw several people that he knew. One of them was T. J., who looked inquiringly at him as he stood in the crowd. Luke caught his eye and made a negative motion with his head, then turned away and waited for the train.

When it stopped, Luke was marched aboard. His escort had been cut down to a sergeant, and two privates to guard him. Before the train left, Luke looked out the window and saw the crowd of spectators still watching. T. J. was gone.

After Luke was in his seat, the sergeant put leg irons on him. Soon the train began to move. As it rolled along Luke began to think about some way of escaping. He knew that Omaha had a secure sandstone guardhouse, and there would be little chance to get away. He wasn't sure what his sentence might be, but he knew it might be months before his case would come up, and he dreaded that time locked up in a cell. They might not even let him have books to pass the time.

As the train rolled along he began thinking, trying to remember just how the toilet was set up on these cars. He closed his eyes and tried to relax and bring to mind everything about them. They were very small, he remembered. There was toilet bowl, a small sink to wash your hands. There was a window, a very small one, and it was usually cracked open to get rid of the smell. He tried to remember just how large it was. He just couldn't recall if it was large enough for a man to slip through. One thing he was sure of, if he was to make his move, it had better be soon before the train carried him out into the middle of nowhere.

Finally he began to groan just a little and hold his belly. Presently the sergeant noticed. "What's the matter?" He finally asked.

"I don't know," Luke said, "but it feels like a couple of wildcats are fighting down there. Bad cramps! Sergeant, I'd better go to the toilet!"

The sergeant thought about it a moment. "All right, I'll take you down."

"Can you take these cuffs off for a minute and let me get out of this coat?" Luke asked.

The sergeant let him remove his heavy coat, then put the handcuffs back on.

The two men got up, and Luke shuffled forward, still in leg irons, and deliberately tripped himself. He went down hard, and got up holding his handcuffed hands to his head, and groaning. A woman, sitting across the aisle had been watching him, and glared at the sergeant. "I don't know what this poor boy had done, but can't you at least take off those leg irons so he can use the toilet!"

The sergeant got red in the face as everyone in the coach glared at him, then began to feel in his pocket for the keys. He bent over and knelt to unlock the leg irons, then escorted Luke to the end of the car. He opened the door for Luke, and said in a low voice, "Take as long as you want, I know how it is when you got the trots. I'll wait outside."

Luke locked the door behind himself, and immediately went to the window. It was about halfway open. He got his cuffed hands beneath it, and shoved upwards. It slid a little, then caught. He put his shoulders behind it then, and shoved with all of his strength. It came, but the opening still looked mighty small. Luke stuck his head through and looked east. Perhaps a mile ahead there appeared to be a grade. If he could get out and drop off as the train slowed on the grade, maybe he could keep from getting hurt. He was glad he had asked the sergeant to let him remove the heavy coat, for he would never have gotten through the small window with it on. He stood on the toilet seat, and was able to grasp an overhead fixture, then raised himself and put his feet through the window. He kept working his wiry body this way and that and finally was able to get one shoulder through, then the other. He had made it. He hung there on the window sill until the train began to slow on the grade, then pushed himself as far away as he could from the side of the car, and fell. He landed with knees bent, and let himself roll, holding his manacled hands up to protect his face. Luke lay there alongside the track as still as death, while the rest of the train thundered on past.

After it was gone, he waited until it went out of sight behind the hill. Then he stood up and checked himself out. Nothing appeared to be broken, but he was scratched and bruised and sore. The handcuffs had hit him on one cheek and it was split open and bleeding. The eye would probably be closed before long, but he was free. All he had to do was make it back to the old man's cabin.

Luke keep waiting for the sound of the train whistle and the scream of brakes, but the only thing he heard was the sound of the train moving away from him. He turned and moved away from the tracks, at a trot, heading across country in the direction of the old man's cabin.

It was then mid-December, and cold. Luke knew he had to somehow make it to the old man's cabin before it got night, or he'd be in trouble without a coat. He kept running, then walking, then trotting, knowing he dared not stop.

When he finally saw Sidney in the distance, he moved around the outskirts, and headed north. Sometimes he thought his heart would burst right through his chest, but he ran on, with dry throat, knowing as soon as the sergeant had missed him, he would telegraph the news from the next station along the line.

He ran onward, walking at times, then trotting, but never stopping until it was dark and he at last saw the shape of the old man's cabin against the clear sky.

The dogs picked up his scent, and began to raise a racket. Luke stopped and waited as the lamp went out and the front door opened. A man moved out into the yard, and Luke heard a cartridge being put into the chamber.

"Who is it?" A voice said. "Sing out!"

"It's me, T. J., Luke," Luke said, and began walking slowly toward the cabin.

"Jesus Christ!" T. J. said in amazement. "Dad, light the lamp! It's Luke!"

The two of them couldn't believe it. They sat him down

and poured a cup of Ol' Pine Top, and looked at the beat-up man in front of them. His bruised eye was closed, his clothing torn, and dried blood covered his face.

"I'd like a cup of water first," Luke said, and the old man brought him one. "What happened?" T. J. asked.

"I got the sergeant to let me go to the toilet, and I was able to wiggle out the window and jump."

"Christ!" T. J. said, looking at Luke's bloody wrists where the manacles had worn the skin completely away. "Dad, how are we goin' to get those cuffs off?"

"I'll get them off," the old man said, "but it'll hurt." He rose and went out to a shed and soon returned with an anvil, hammer, and chisel.

"You better have that drink, now," T. J. said.

It was painful, but the cuffs came off, and they cleaned his bloody wrists, and put salve and bandages on them.

Luke was half drunk, by the time the cuffs were off, but he said, "T. J., I got to put some miles behind me before morning."

"You're in no shape to travel!"

"They'll be scouring the country, friend, I got to go."

"All right, I'll go saddle the horses. Dad will fix you something to eat, then we'll get our bedrolls and go."

And go they did. After saying goodby to the old man, they rode around Sidney and crossing Lodgepole Creek, headed south into Colorado.

Luke was to say later that it was the longest ride of his life. When he began falling out of the saddle, T. J. tied his feet beneath the horse's belly, and led his horse with Luke slumped in the saddle completely out.

The next day they holed up and rested and Luke regained

some of his strength. They rode, more leisurely now, sold their horses at the first settlement, then took a stage into Denver.[2]

CHAPTER FIFTEEN

The first thing Luke and T. J. did in Denver was to take a room at a good hotel and get cleaned up. They bought new clothing and boots, took a long soak in the bathtub, and got into their new duds. Luke's wound along his ribs from the .45 slug, had broken open when he had jumped from the train, and was painful and inflamed, so the partners found a doctor who treated the bullet wound and his wrists where the metal handcuffs had chaffed him so badly. The doctor put on new bandages and told Luke to come back every morning.

T. J. began checking out the town, but Luke knew he needed to just rest and get back his strength. He had T. J. pick up newspapers at the newsstands from Sidney, Ogallala and Omaha, and kept looking for any mention of his arrest or a report of his escape from the train. None of the papers mentioned any of this, and he was left to wonder why. The only thing he could think was perhaps the army had been so embarrassed at his escape, they had not reported it to Omaha, or maybe the sergeant in charge of him on the train, had carried the papers with him, and after the escape had simply gotten off the train at Ogallala, and returned to Camp Robinson. A week or so went by and still there was nothing in the papers. Luke put it out of his mind, for he couldn't see the army coming to a teeming city like Denver to look for him.[1]

The time Luke spent in the hotel healing gave him time to review the past two years. Looking back, he could see what a dangerous enterprise he and T. J. had embarked upon. It had paid off big however, and from fifteen months trading with the Sioux and Cheyennes, together with the money he'd already saved, he had just a little more than $60,000 in the bank.[2] At last he had finally achieved his dream of becoming a full-time professional gambler, a dream which had been born as a thirteen-year-old cowboy in Abilene when he'd first seen Dick Clark dealing at the Alamo. He could go on dealing for others, and free-lance on the side, but when the opportunity came, he had enough money now to bank his own game.

The realization that he had finally realized his goal, transformed him in some manner. The long, hard days and nights pushing longhorn cattle up the trail, cold, wet bedding, squatting around a wind-blown fire eating cold beans, stampedes in the night, and the overall dreariness were in the past. So too was the memory of buffalo hunting, skinning the huge beasts, the smell of death and rot that permeated the whole prairie, the heat in summer and the bitter cold of winter, the filthy blood and grease-stained duck clothing, and most of all, the constant scratching for lice and other vermin.

There might be bad days ahead; he knew there would be, but it would be different, a new life, and he went into it expectantly. Never again would he wear work clothes or have his hands torn by the reata as he made a dally around a saddle horn. No more scouting or dispatch riding, never again would he endure the loneliness of an isolated camp. His life from now on would be in the boomtowns and cities where things were happening.

He began thinking about replacing the pistol which had been taken from him in Nebraska. A professional gambler was always being challenged by some sore loser, a drunk, or just a bully, and had to be prepared to take care of himself and keep order in his games.

Previously, Luke had sometimes carried a pistol in a shoulder holster, or in a traditional gunbelt worn beneath a frock coat. Both of these methods were bulky and uncomfortable, and the weapon showed. Gambling halls were often hot in the summers, and you dealt in just a vest. What Luke wanted was a weapon that was comfortable to wear, wouldn't show, and was easy to draw if he needed it.

When he began to feel better, he went to a custom gunsmith and laid out his problem. He told the man he was comfortable with a Colt .45, and wondered if it were possible to shorten the barrel so the revolver could be carried in a special holster sewn into the place where his right hand hip pocket would be on a pair of suit trousers.

That was no problem, the gunsmith said, and brought out a new Colt; he told Luke that he could indeed shorten the barrel. The man then queried him about what kind of a front sight he wanted on it. Luke asked for a small gold sight that sloped back so that it would come out of the holster easily without hanging up. Luke also asked the gunsmith to hone and fine-tune the trigger sear.

It would be done exactly the way he wanted, the gunsmith said, and Luke paid for the pistol and the custom work in advance.

When the Colt was ready, he took it to Bascom and Stearns, well-known custom tailors in Denver. To show them that he was good for anything he ordered, he pulled out a roll of bills and advanced them $500, then asked to see some of their material. Bolts of cloth were unrolled before him onto the counter, and he picked out several different colors and materials. He told the tailors what he wanted in all of the trousers in place of the right hand hip pocket. He left the newly altered Colt with them, and asked for their opinion on the built-in pistol holster. They suggested a holster of soft leather which wouldn't be bulky when he wasn't armed and leaned back in a chair, but which would be stiff enough to support the Colt when it was being worn. Luke wanted the Colt to ride high enough on his hip to be covered by his vests. The tailor suggested the vests be cut long enough to cover the pistol butt. All this was soon settled, and the tailor measured him and he soon was back in the hotel.

Luke and T. J. had moved to the elegant Charpiot's Hotel, on Larimer Street, and were soon busy taking in the sights of Denver. When Luke's suits were ready, he tried them on and was immensely pleased with the way they fitted. One day he and his partner went into the restaurant and got some empty tin cans. Luke picked up his new Colt and a couple of boxes of cartridges, then hired a hack and they drove out to the city dump.

T. J. set up a row of cans, and Luke loaded up and began shooting. He knew with the Colt's barrel shortened, it wouldn't be accurate at any distance, but from now on, if he did any shooting, it would very likely be at close range anyway. Luke was satisfied with the way the Colt handled, and began practicing drawing the Colt from the special sewn in holster on his hip. He had dusted the inside of the holster with talcum powder, and the Colt came out smoothly. His vest covered the butt of the Colt, and with the vest unbuttoned and hanging loose, he was able to draw and shoot fairly fast. All he would need was practice and getting used to the balance of the shortened revolver.

Although the new silver town of Leadville, was fast becoming the mining capitol, Denver had long sported first class saloons and gambling houses. Ed Chase, the brother of the man Luke had worked for in Cheyenne, had long been the premier gambling hall and saloon operator in Denver. He had owned the Progressive Club, and also the Palace. Ed

Chase's partner in The Palace in Denver was Ed Gaylord. Later, Ed Chase and Vaso Chucovich would open the lavish Navarre for the wealthy who had money to burn—or gamble away.

Another famous saloon and gambling hall owner, was a former Pony Express rider, named Billy Cates, and he operated his Cates Club on Curtis Street. Cates put his profits into ranchland that soon was worth a fortune. When Billy Cates was dying in 1911, he called his friend, Ed Chase, to his bedside and asked him to distribute his fortune as he saw fit to old broken-down former gamblers. "There are plenty of folks to help women and children," Cates told Chase, "but who cares about broken-down old men with no money?"[3]

Most of these topnotch gambling operations were honest, and their owners took much pride in their reputations. Just a hint of crooked dealing was enough to ruin the reputation of such an establishment. They didn't have to cheat; the house percentages and other income from the saloons and hotels were enough to make them gold mines.

Luke and T. J. played the tables, and went to the opera house, to the vaudeville shows, and ate at the best restaurants. Luke found bookshops almost as good as New York City's, and was content.

One day T. J. said out of the blue, "Think I'll go back to Texas, pardner."

Luke nodded. "And do what?"

"Well, we've had some excitement, and made a lot of money, but now it's over, and I think I'll go back to Austin and go to work."

"Doing what?" Luke asked.

"I don't think I ever told you, but my daddy owns a bank. He always gave me money . . . and I just spent it and had a good time. I think he just kinda gave up on me. Up there in Nebraska with you, I worked harder than I ever have before, and I proved something to myself. Now I think I'll go home and ask my daddy for a job."

"Which way you going?" Luke asked.

T. J. grinned. "I sure ain't goin' back through Nebraska."

"Well, maybe I'll ride with you as far as Pueblo," Luke said, "I've been thinking about Leadville. Sounds like things are really booming there."

The next day, the two men took a hack to the train station, and caught the Denver and Rio Grande south for Pueblo. There the partners shook hands, and said goodby. T. J. rode on south to the end of the line in New Mexico Territory, and took a stagecoach south and east into Texas. Luke stayed overnight in Pueblo, then caught a coach on to Leadville the next morning. The two men wouldn't meet again for ten years. When they did, T. J. would be a portly, successful banker, and Luke would be one of the most widely known big time gamblers in the southwest.

CHAPTER SIXTEEN

Back in the 1860's Abe Lee had found gold not far from the headwaters of the Arkansas River in central Colorado in a place called California Gulch. The gold was located on the western slope of the Mosquito Mountain Range, and mining only lasted about two years. Will Stevens had also come to the gulch about the time the gold was petering out, and the miners were leaving in droves. Stevens, a surveyor by trade, soon packed up his equipment, and left, too. He took a job over in Utah and worked there for several years, laying out section corners and building monuments, but he kept thinking about California Gulch. Something told him there was still gold there, somewhere. Finally in 1874, Stevens came back and stopped by Horace Tabor's little store in Oro City, where Tabor and his wife, Augusta, had hung on. Tabor sold supplies to the few dozen miners left, and Augusta baked pies and fed many of the bachelors still in the gulch. Stevens queried Tabor on what was going on, and Tabor told him of some twenty men who owned mining claims and had banded together and were digging a ditch in order to increase the supply of water needed for their placer operations.

Stevens took a walk up the gulch and looked over the claims of the miners, and inspected the ditch they were digging. What he saw of their claims impressed him enough to write a geologist friend back in Michigan, one Alvinus

Wood, and persuade him to come to Colorado to look the claims over.

Evidently the two men thought they could make a little money there, and they soon raised $50,000 and bought out all twenty miners. They immediately hired the same men to continue digging the water ditch they would need for their placer operation.

A year later they hadn't struck the Mother Lode, but they had received a thirty percent return on their investment. One of the problems with the way they were running their operation, was the tremendous amount of black sand which clogged their sluice boxes— sand that had to be laboriously shoveled out of the way by hand. One day, Al Wood stood studying the annoying sand. Something about it intrigued him; he collected several different samples, and took them back to their cabin and ran an assay test on them. The samples of black sand turned out to be carbonate of lead, and assayed forty dollars of silver to the ton. Wood quickly went up the gulch to where his partner worked with the other hired miners, got him aside and told him the news.

Without delay the partners followed the trace of black sand up the mountain, to a vein of dirty black rock ten feet deep. They immediately staked a claim and had it recorded, then moved their miners to began to work the face of the vein.

Some weeks later, one of the Irish miners, got Stevens aside and said: "I'm curious, sir, about why we are piling up all that dirty black rock down there on the flat . . . you know there isn't a trace of color in the whole batch!"

Stevens knew the secret would soon be out when they started shipping the ore, and he decided to let the man, whose name was Walls, in on the fact.

"You're absolutely right about the ore not containing any gold, my friend, but that black rock you've been cussing is carbonate of lead, and is full of silver."

Needless to say, the Irishman soon quit and had staked his own claim, and the silver rush was on.

By the summer of 1877, California Gulch was aswarm with prospectors from all walks of life, each determined to make his fortune. Many of them did in various ways. It wasn't long before Stray Horse and Evans' Gulches were staked, then Fryer's Hill, and the principal silver mines were named: Stevens, Moyer, Minnie, A.Y., Printer Boy, Maid of Irin, Morning Star, Wolftone, and Highland Mary. There were the Little Jonny, Rough and Ready, Camp Bird, Robert Emmet, El Paso, Robert E. Lee, Matchless, Little Pittsburg, New Discovery, Little Chief, Chrystolite, and Coronado.

George Fryer opened up a great body of ore on top of what would be Fryer's Hill. John Champion, a Canadian, followed a bunch of other prospectors up into scrubby pine hills. Champion didn't know the first thing about prospecting, but he was there at the right moment. He ran around like a wild man, as more knowledgeable prospectors began to stake claims. After awhile he stood there dumbly, for it all looked the same to him. In desperation, he finally approached an old prospector who looked like he knew what he was doing, and asked plaintively, "Where should I dig?"

The prospector looked at the Canadian in annoyance and, just to get rid of him, pointed to a scrub pine about as far away as he could see, and said, "Over there, under that tree!"

The appreciative greenhorn dashed away and began to dig in the spot indicated. In a matter of hours John Champion was a wealthy man; the Little Jonny was to become one of the richest lodes around California Gulch.

The new town finally got its name in January, 1878. A group of miners met in Gilbert's wagon shop, and suggested names for the new community; Oro City just didn't sound right anymore. One man suggested Carbonateville, but that didn't sound very classy; another was for Agassiz, the renowned geologist and naturalist. Agassiz was also rejected. "What about just calling it Leadville?" another man suggested, and Leadville it became.

Because Tabor's store was the town meeting place, the group voted him mayor, and in time his store became town hall and post office, and Tabor became postmaster. Tabor loved being at the center of things, but stayed out of the scrambling for a claim. He and Augusta had worked claims before, and all they had to show for it were calluses from the pick and shovel handles. In fact, Augusta, had shoveled aside tons of that black sand that used to clog up the placer chute, the sand that was now rich in silver.

Tabor was content to sort the mail and to sell all sorts of things from his store to the prospectors. Indeed, he might well have spent the rest of his days there, but for his own generosity.

In April, 1878, Tabor and a few others were sitting around his store smoking and discussing the word that morning of George Fryer's rich strike on the hill. On the edge of the group, were two prospectors who Tabor had known since his South Park days. They were named George Hook and August Rische. Hook was originally from Pittsburgh, and had met Rische on his way to Colorado years before. In all the years they had searched for gold, it seemed to elude them, and all they had to show for the backbreaking work were calluses, and rheumatism from standing in icy mountain streams panning for gold.

Now, as the two men listened to the talk, they again began to feel the excitement which only the discovery of precious metals seem to give, and after they went back to their cabin that night they decided to give it another try. Early next morning, a Sunday, they took their protesting bodies up to Fryer's Hill and stood looking at Fryer's New Discovery contact. They both agreed that the carbonate must have sometime in the past come off the highlands behind, and they went back down to Tabor's store, and put the touch on him again for a grubstake.

They had not paid Tabor for the previous one, but the storekeeper was known to have a soft heart, and Hook said: "Horace, we think we know where that carbonate is coming from up at Fryer's contact, would you grubstake us again, to look for it?"

Tabor probably agreed more to get rid of them than anything. As the partners picked out the things they needed, things like bacon, beans, flour, some blasting powder and fuses, Hook told Tabor when they found the lode he would be a full partner and own a third share. Tabor nodded absently as he sorted the mail; he'd heard that one before, too. Then, Hook asked, "Could we also have a jug of whiskey? It's still cold up there in the evenings."

Again Tabor nodded, and the partners put their purchases into a sack, some seventeen dollars worth, and left, grinning and nudging one another on getting the whiskey, too.

They climbed the hill behind the New Discovery, where Fryer already had a crew of miners digging. By the time they were high above Fryer's, and a little south, they sank down out of breath beneath a scrub pine to rest. "Do you think it's too early to have a little toss?" Rische asked his partner.

"Hell, the sun's over the yardarm, isn't it?" Hook said, and dug out the stone jug of whiskey.

One toss led to another, and as Rische looked farther up the slope he began to dread the climb. "Where do you think we ought to start digging?" he asked his partner.

Hook had been looking up, too, and feeling content with the whiskey, said, "How about right here."

"Suits me," Rische said with relief.

They began sinking a shaft, and a month later hit a vein of high-grade carbonate ore. Hook named the new mine, Little

Pittsburgh, and it wasn't long before the three partners were taking out $8,000 a week. This sudden wealth seemed to unnerve Hook, and he soon sold out to Rische and Tabor. It wasn't long before Rische began to worry that the rich lode might dry up, and he, too, sold out.[1]

But the plodding Tabor wasn't going to let this chance get away from him, and parlayed this strike into one after another rich mines. At one point a miner salted what he thought was a washed out mine, with ore he had stolen from Taber's own Little Pittsburgh, and sold it to Tabor. Then the man told everyone what he had done, and the whole mining camp laughed at the gullible Tabor.

Tabor paid no attention to the laughter, and hired a crew of miners to deepen the shaft of the Christolite. The laughter stopped abruptly when Tabor's men struck a rich vein only eight feet deeper than the jokester had dug.

From just getting by, Tabor's income rose like a hot air balloon. Soon he was buying stock in various enterprises. He also began to build the first brick building in Leadville, and organized a company of volunteer firemen who proudly wore scarlet uniforms with Tabor's name on their chests. He built a firehouse, and ordered a pumping machine and special fire hoses from San Francisco.

The money poured in for Tabor, and the silver town expanded in every direction. As more stores, saloons, and gambling houses began going up, more and more people flocked to the carbonate bonanza. The bulk of the miners were Irish and Welchmen, a hard working and hard drinking bunch they were, too, full of fun and fights and laughter. The Welchmen were called Cousin Jacks, and when they began sending for their families, their wives were called, Cousin Jennies.

Sawmills sprang up, trying in vain to supply the demand for lumber. Guards were needed to watch the lumber which would otherwise be immediately stolen. Thieves and pickpockets soon found their way to the easy pickings. Finally, the town fathers had to get a town marshal and a herd of assistants to handle the crime, but before that a vigilante group strung up some of these crooks.

More hotels and restaurants were soon built, but were forever full, and tent flophouses sometimes charged so much an hour for the weary who couldn't afford a hotel room.

The payroll from the mines soon was over a half-million dollars a month, and money flowed like water. Saloons, usually one of the first businesses in any boomtown, sprouted like weeds, and lined the streets. Gambling halls were usually operated in connection with the saloons, and of course, the women of the night were soon there to get their share, coming from Kansas City, St. Louis, New Orleans, and as far away as New York City. Bill Bush, of Central City, came to Leadville to build a three story hotel he called the Clarendon, and the ubiquitous Horace Tabor was soon into building the Tabor Opera House just across the street from the magnificent Clarendon. Eventually there was a covered passageway that allowed hotel guests and theater patrons to make the crossing without getting mud on their evening clothing, and to keep the bitter winter winds from lifting the ladies' skirts.

* * *

It was into this teeming City of Silver, a burgeoning city of excesses, Luke Short came to build his career as a full-time professional gambler, in the early months of 1879. He found a fair hotel room for a price, but that was no problem for he was flush with money. He got settled in and began to look around him. Leadville had a population, one of the newspapers guessed, to be around 35,000. The miners were making four dollars a day, had plenty of money to spend, and seemed to be bent on getting rid of it.

Luke decided he hadn't come to the wrong spot, for money flowed everywhere like water. After roaming the saloons and gambling halls, he knew Leadville was made for him. The town was at an elevation of more than 10,000 feet, and when the miners got off shift and descended to the streets, they cleaned up as best they could, then ate and were drawn to the light and warmth of the saloons and gambling halls with money in their pockets waiting to be spent.

Soon as Luke was settled, he went to work getting his share of the wealth. As befitting his new profession, he was fashionably dressed in a pearl-grey suit, and a grey derby to match. One night, as he bucked the tiger in a gambling hall, he ran into trouble. He was a small man, to begin with and, all dressed up and wearing a derby, might have appeared to be a dude from back east. A rough looking type standing behind Luke at the faro layout kept making fun of Luke's clothes. Luke ignored him, until the man knocked his derby off, and stood there grinning at him, daring him to do something about it. Things hadn't changed; bullies were the same as they had been at his school in Texas.

Luke whirled around and drew his short barreled Colt and had it cocked and centered between the man's eyes before he knew what had happened. Luke made the man pick up his hat and dust it off to his satisfaction before returning it to his head.

The jokester, his face white with fear, backed into the crowd of onlookers, and soon was gone.

Several days later another man, not knowing what had happened to the first, did the same thing. This time Luke pistol-whipped the man, leaving him unconscious on the floor with a deep cut over one eye.

While Luke was dusting off his derby, the owner of the

saloon came up and touched his arm and invited him to a table in back for a drink.

"Nice work," the saloon owner said, after pouring them drinks. "What line of work do you do, if I may ask?"

"I'm a gambler," Luke said.

The owner asked him where he had worked, and Luke told him that he had managed the Long Branch Gambling concession in Dodge City for two years during the summer seasons, and had worked for Joe Bassett at the Marble Hall in Kansas City, at Sidney and Ogallala, in Nebraska, and for John Chase in Cheyenne.

"Do you want a job dealing?"

"I just got to town," Luke said, "I kinda thought I'd just free-lance for awhile."

"This is a rough town, with troublemakers from all over the world. One of my top dealers quit last night, finally got tired of sore losers and troublemakers sticking a gun in his face. I'd sure pay you top wages, and a percentage of what you take in, if you'd deal here for me."

Luke thought about it. Maybe that was the way to do it here in Leadville, deal for awhile. He could buck the tiger on his time off. "I might take the job," he said, "if I could do a little gambling on my own, on the side."

"That would be fine with me," the man said, "as long as you don't play against the house here."

"Of course," Luke said, and they shook on it.

Luke dealt for several weeks without serious trouble. Then one night a man named Brown came in and began to play faro at Luke's table. The man had been there before and was always a quarrelsome player, disregarding rules, and tampering with other players' bets. On this night he'd been drinking, and was particularly troublesome. Instinct told Luke there would soon be serious trouble, and as unobtrusively as he could he moved his Jürgensen watch, and unbuttoned his vest.

The play went on and the troublemaker kept moving his bets after the call. Luke warned him several times, but he persisted, and Luke finally told him to cash in his chips and leave the table.

Brown began cursing Luke, then reached for his pistol. All of the other players dove away from the table, and Luke fired point blank. The heavy .45 slug caught Brown in one cheek and passed across and exited the far jaw. It was a hellish wound. Brown slumped across the faro table, bleeding profusely, and Luke thought he had killed him, but he began to moan.

Luke looked at two of Brown's friends, and told them to take him away if they wanted to get him to a doctor, and they lifted Brown up and dragged him out.

Luke holstered his Colt, then called for the Negro swamper to clean the blood from the table. "Gentlemen," he said to the other startled players, "let's adjourn to the bar for a drink on the house. As soon as the layout is cleaned, we'll begin with a fresh deck of cards."[2]

Charges were soon dropped against Luke when other players who had witnessed the shooting testified. Brown lived, but didn't make any make more trouble in Leadville. He left soon afterward.

The word soon spread that Luke was not to be trifled with, and his stock in the gambling fraternity went up.

* * *

The golden age of the gambler in the West was perhaps between the middle 1860's following the Civil War, and the middle 1880's when the antigambling and temperance movement came to the fore, as the frontier cow, mining, and railroad towns were settled by the wives of businessmen and settlers. These women, together with the church groups and preachers, did, in the end prevail, but while it lasted the big time gambler was one of the most respected professionals in the community. The great popularity of gambling games in the frontier West, and the perceived need for professional gamblers was inevitable and predictable. It was a time when everyone, in a sense, was a gambler. Pioneer men and women gambled they could get across the plains safely in their covered wagons to a new home in Oregon, Utah, or California. They gambled their children would survive the trip, though many did not. The moneyless Texans gambled they could get their herds of longhorns to a market in Kansas after the war; miners often gambled they could find the precious metal that would make their fortunes. So, gambling on the turn of a card didn't seem that much more of a gamble.

The Indians had gambled from time immemorial, taking their chances on the throw of a handful of sticks or pebbles; Cortez's men had gambled over the golden riches that they took from the Aztecs. Gambling in the United States probably began in wayside taverns along the eastern seaboard where travelers stopped for the night, then gradually followed the settlers west.

Various games were popular during the big gambling era. Two of the most popular were *Vingt Et Un,* a French importation, which the Americans began to call Twenty-one. The French also brought faro, originally, pharaoh, which often bore the likeness of a tiger, hence the phrase, "Buck the Tiger." In the 1870's, poker began to be a major game, but the quick turns of faro continued to be popular. Actually, honest faro games, in the better gambling houses, gave the faro player an almost even chance to win. The only advantage the house had, was that if a pair came on a turn, the house took half of all bets.

The faro layout was on a green felt, or green painted board, with ace through king displayed in spades. The suits didn't matter, only the face value. The player put down his chips on the card, or cards, he wanted to bet on, and the dealer dealt a "turn"—two cards from a standard deck of 52. The object was for the player to predict which cards would appear. The first card of the turn lost for the player, and won for the house. The second card won for the player. The bettor's chips were placed on the card's image, and bet the card would win. Players could bet a card would lose by putting a hexagonal copper token on top of his chips. Players could bet on any number of cards, and hedge their bets in that manner; they could also change their bets between turns. The turns were dealt from a metal box, face up, two cards to a turn. The top card was a "dead" card, and was called the "soda card." The last card was also dead, and called "hock." The term, "from soda to hock," meant, from beginning to end.

A lookout was often employed by the house to keep players from cheating, and to collect and pay off bets. A "casekeeper" was also used; this was an abacuslike wooden frame with miniature cards matching the ones on the layout. From each card there was a spindle with four buttons that could be moved to indicate how many cards of each value had been played, as the dealer went through the turns.

It sounds complicated, but was, in fact, a simple game to play. For many years faro was the premier game in the West; high rolling gamblers liked the easy odds, and the fast action. It was a quiet game, and was played by everyone from mining magnates to newsboys and shoeshine urchins in the mining camps of the West.

Poker was also becoming a popular game, and Luke Short liked it possibly better that faro, for real skill could be used here where a memory for cards already played, and a knowledge of the odds helped immensely.

In the spring of 1879, Luke was paid $200 a week, plus a

percentage of the money his table took in. This was while the Cousin Jacks from Wales and the Irishers were being paid four dollars for ten hour shifts in the mines. In addition Luke would buck the tiger, or play poker in his time off at other gambling establishments. He was soon known as a high roller, for with his personal bank behind him, he could take an occasional loss, and go right back to playing. Soon he was playing big stake games with the Carbonate Kings themselves. On one spectacular night he took $10,000 from Horace Tabor in an all-night poker game.[3]

His bank account kept growing, and he was just waiting for the right opportunity to buy a piece of a gambling hall, or to own one outright, but that would take more than he had right now, especially in high priced Leadville.

It was in the spring of that year when Bill Harris and Chalk Beeson learned Luke was in Leadville, and wired him an attractive offer to come manage the gambling rooms at the Long Branch once more for the coming cattle season.

Luke decided to accept the offer, and said goodby to all the friends he had made in Leadville, then headed south and east to Dodge City.

Luke soon settled back into his job of managing the gambling at the Long Branch Saloon. His close friend, Sheriff Bat Masterson, brought him up to date on the affairs of Ford County in his absence. One of which was his orders to pick up several of Dull Knife's Indians who were accused of murder during their breakout in Indian Territory the previous summer.

Luke then, told Bat about his part in chasing Dull Knife and Little Wolf in Nebraska with Major Thornburgh. This of course, led to his trading post venture with T. J., and of his subsequent arrest and escape from the train. Luke showed Bat the scars around his wrists from the handcuffs.

All this appealed to Masterson's sense of humor, and he

laughed at the picture of Luke squeezing through the toilet window on the train, and jumping.

"So now," laughed the Sheriff of Ford County, "you are wanted by the entire Army of the Platte, as an escaped bootlegger!"

"I guess so," Luke said blandly, at which Bat broke up completely.

Bat Masterson loved a joke better than most men, and one day he and Wyatt Earp came to Luke with an idea for a prank.

Both Bat and Wyatt had taken the Reverend O. W. Wright under their protection when he had arrived in Dodge. They had helped collect funds from the saloons, gambling halls and prostitutes to build his church. Now, Bat and Wyatt told Luke, the Ladies Aid Society wanted to hold a baby beauty contest to raise money for their missionary fund.

Luke told his two friends he would put up one hundred dollars in gold for the winning baby's mother. Bat and Wyatt took these funds to the Ladies Aid Society and together established the rules for the contest. The babies had to be born in Dodge City and be less than one year of age. The winner was to be determined by ballots to be sold six for a quarter.

Many of the ladies had infants of their own and surely expected to win the one hundred dollar prize. The society had ballots printed up and distributed throughout Dodge City. As ballots were bought, the buyers wrote in the name of the baby they were voting for.

The ladies were, of course, unaware that Bat, Wyatt and Luke had already picked out their winner as the ballots were distributed. The baby's mother was a huge black woman who worked in a Negro dance hall on the other side of the railroad tracks, and as the word spread to the cowboys and sporting crowd, they bought tickets in the baby's name with great gusto.

On the final day of the contest, the Ladies Aid Society held a church supper, and the Reverend Wright announced that more than $2,000 had been raised for the missionary fund. All the audience applauded, and the ladies who had their babies entered in the contest, sat expectantly as they waited for their minister to announce the winning baby's name.

The Reverend Wright started with the names of the babies with the least number of votes. Gradually he worked up the list to the winning baby's name, but when the winner was announced, no one was familiar with the baby.

There was confusion now. "Is the mother of the winning baby present?" asked the Reverend Wright.

"I believe she is just outside the door, Reverend!" Masterson shouted. A moment later Bat and Wyatt ushered in the baby's mother, who held in her arms the little black winner. The cowboys and sporting men in the back of the church whooped and hollered, and one of the indignant women rose and, in a loud voice, angrily demanded to know who the father was.

The red-faced minister was stymied for a moment, then declared, "That is this lady's business!" He then handed over the sack of gold pieces.

At this, the men in the rear of the church broke up completely, then went off to their favorite saloons and gambling holes to chuckle over the joke.

Back in February, The Governor of Kansas, G. T. Anthony, had requested the army to turn the renegade Cheyennes of Dull Knife's band over to the State of Kansas to stand trial for the murders they had committed after breaking out of their reservation in Indian Territory. The Indian's names were: Wild Hog, Old Crow, Big Head, Left Hand, Blacksmith, Porcupine, and Nosey Walker. Bat had taken Charlie Bassett and his younger brother, Jim Masterson, to Leavenworth to pick up the Cheyennes and return them to Dodge for trial.

The Indians were lodged in the jail for four months, but a change of venue forced Bat to take them to Lawrence. The case was finally dismissed because of lack of witnesses and evidence, and this was to cause Masterson much trouble.

In March, Bat was asked by the Atchison, Topeka, and Sante Fe Railroad, if he would gather some men and protect the Sante Fe's right-of-way over in the Royal Gorge, in Colorado. The Sante Fe and the Denver and Rio Grande Railroad were fighting over who would get into Leadville first. It is hard to understand by what authority Masterson, as sheriff of Ford County, could intervene in the dispute between the two railroads, but Bat was also a United States Deputy Marshal, and perhaps the Sante Fe thought he might have the authority. Anyway, Bat picked a bunch of gunslingers, and headed west. The would-be posse had a great time drinking and gambling, and even did a little fighting with the Denver and Rio Grande's hardcases. Only one of the Dodge City bunch was shot, a man named Henry Jenkins.

In the end the court awarded the right-of-way to the Denver line, and they paid the Sante Fe $1,400,000 for the work all ready done in the gorge.

When Bat got back to Dodge he began trying to collect the $7,000 worth of bills he had run up bringing the seven Cheyenne prisoners from Leavenworth to Dodge, then to Lawrence for the trial, as well as for all the expenses to guard and feed the Indians. Now, some of the people blamed Bat for all the bills against Ford County, pointing out the Indians had been let off with no punishment. This was not Bat's fault, of course, but by the time the fall election came around, he was defeated because of it.

It left him bitter, and in January, when his term was up, he was ready to leave Dodge City.

Back in the fall, Wyatt Earp had also resigned as Assistant City Marshal of Dodge, and prepared to leave. He told Bat that he was tired of risking his life for the money he was being paid. He planned on moving to Tombstone, Arizona Territory, where the big silver strike was. His brother, Virgil, was already there and interested in a silver mine. Little did Wyatt realize that he would soon be involved in the most bitter conflict of his career.

By that time the cattle shipping season was about over, and Luke Short had returned to Leadville. Before he left he talked to Bat about leaving police work for good, and concentrating solely upon gambling, for he knew that Bat was a good gambler. Bat said he thought that was what he would do, and as soon as his term was over he followed Luke to Leadville, and was soon successfully making the circuit of Denver, Cheyenne, Deadwood, Ogallala, and Kansas City.

It should be pointed out that after many years of knocking around the frontier, doing various things, Masterson and Luke Short were only in their mid-twenties.

Luke spent the rest of 1879 running games in Leadville. During the following year he began to free lance again, gambling along the same circuit that Bat was on. Often they were together in the same town. Bat was doing well as professional gambler, but unlike both Luke and Wyatt Earp, he always had trouble keeping the money he won.

Luke was back in Leadville in the last months of 1880, when Wyatt Earp's wire found him. Wyatt had an interest in the Oriental Gambling Hall in Tombstone, and he and his partners were making money hand over fist; the problem was that the opposition was sending in some pretty rough characters to disrupt their games. Wyatt asked Luke to come to Tombstone and take over one of the tables and put a stop to this harassment. Wyatt also mentioned that Bat would be coming from Kansas City to help him out as well.

Luke had been hearing a lot about Tombstone; he also was looking forward to seeing both Bat and Wyatt again, as well as his old friend, Dick Clark, and his former boss, Bill Harris of Dodge City, who were now partners with Wyatt in the Oriental.

Luke Short at 23, after his trail
driving and buffalo hunting days
(From an old tintype)

Luke Short about 1883

This photo of Luke Short appeared in
newspapers of the day, and was
captioned: "Luke Short, the famous
frontier gambler—dressed for a trip to
the States"

THE FAMOUS DODGE CITY PEACE COMMISSION IN 1883
Back row, Left to right: W. H. Harris, Luke Short, Bat Masterson, W. F. Petillion.
Front row: C. E. Bassett, Wyatt Earp, M. F. McLain, Neil Brown

Short Photo Collection

Henry Short—grandfather of the author,
and younger brother of Luke Short

CHAPTER SEVENTEEN

About the same time the miners were flocking to the carbonate rich gulches and hills of the Colorado highland around Leadville, there was a lone man in southeastern Arizona on the verge of another silver strike. It was in April of 1877 that Ed Schieffelin came to the area. Ed, a thirty-year-old lone wolf prospector, signed on with the army which was starting up a post that was to be called Fort Huachuca. It was located west of the San Pedro River near the north end of the Huachuca Mountains. The Apaches still dominated the area, and Schieffelin had signed on as a scout in order to get into the area with some protection.

One day on patrol northeast of the San Pedro, Schieffelin picked up what looked like silver float. He put it away in his saddlebags and marked the spot on his map. Later he made a trip alone back into the area. The soldiers kidded Ed, telling him Chiricahuas in the Dragoons, would have his scalp, and the only thing he'd find was his tombstone.

The mineral belt in the San Pedro Valley had been caused by a local upheaval long in the past. The upheaval of porphyry came through a capping of limestone, and it was this area of upheaval that Schieffelin was searching for. He was careful of Apache sign as he searched the gullies and ridges looking for the spot where the silver float had broken loose and been washed down by the summer monsoons.

Eventually Ed found some promising samples which he broke off with his pick and put into his saddlebags. He was flat broke and about out of grub, so he headed northwest to Globe where his brother, Al, worked in the Silver King Mine. Ed got a job there and finally talked his brother and a mining engineer into returning to his find.

The next spring the mining engineer named Gird, built a crude furnace in an abandoned cabin built by prospectors, who had been killed by the Apaches, and found some of their samples assayed $15,000 a ton. Ed named the mine from which the sample came the Lucky Cuss. The next claim they staked was called the Tough Nut, and the rush was on.

The site chosen for the town, which would later be named Tombstone, was then called Goose Flats. It was 4500 feet above sea level, and by fall of 1879 had a population of about a thousand people. In 1880 the Southern Pacific pushed their rails east across the Colorado River to Tucson, and freight and mail were carried by wagons to the booming silver town. As with any boomtown, saloons and gambling establishments were among the first buildings built, followed by restaurants, hotels, and grocery stores. Telegraph service also was established in 1880, and many thought Tombstone would become the capitol of Arizona Territory.[1]

Like any booming town where money was to be made, the various factions began forming. In Tombstone there were two elements clearly divided, and at odds with one another. John Behan, as sheriff was said to have a lucrative position which was worth more than $40,000 a year. One of Behan's duties was collecting taxes, a portion of which he was able to keep. On Behan's side, were the "cowboys," mainly Curly Bill Brocius, the Clanton family, headed by Old Man Clanton, the McLaury brothers, Frank Stilwell, Pete Spence, Zwing Hunt, Jim Crane, Billy Grounds, Bill Leonards and others who ran some cattle along the San Pedro, but, according to the

Tombstone *Epitaph*, "ran other peoples' cattle more than they did their own." The *Epitaph* also declared that "cowboy" was synonymous with stock thief, holdup man, and murderer.

On the other side of the fence was John Clum, one time Indian agent, mayor of Tombstone, and editor of the *Epitaph*. Allied with Clum, were Wells Fargo and Company, the Southern Pacific Railroad which was building west to east, other business people in Tombstone, as well as Wyatt, Virgil, and Morgan Earp, Doc Holliday, and other sympathizers.

In 1880 a well-known trio formed a partnership in Tombstone; they were Lou Rickabaugh, a San Francisco gambler, Dick Harris, still a partner in the Long Branch Saloon in Dodge City, and Dick Clark. The three sporting men had leased the gambling part of the Oriental Building on Allen and Fifth Streets from Milt Joyce. Joyce, who was also called Mike by some, operated the Oriental Saloon with the help of his bartender, Buckskin Frank Leslie.[2]

After signing the lease with Joyce, the three partners sent to San Francisco for materials, and began refurbishing the rear of the building which would be the gambling hall. Finally, in July of 1880, they had their grand opening.

The *Epitaph* stated this about the Oriental opening:

"Last evening the portals were thrown open and the public permitted to gaze upon the most elegantly furnished saloon this side of the favored city of the Golden Gate. Twenty-eight burners suspended in neat chandeliers afforded an illumination of ample brilliance, and the bright rays reflected from the many colored crystals on the bar sprinkled like December icing in the sunshine. The saloon comprises two apartments. To the right of the main entrance is the bar, beautifully carved, finished in white and gilt and capped with a handsomely polished top. In the rear of this stands a brace of sideboards which are simply elegant and must be seen to be appreciated. . . .

"The back apartment is covered with a brilliant Brussels carpet, and suitably furnished after a style of a grand club room with conveniences for the wily dealers in polished ivory. . . . "

The Oriental became so popular other gamblers in town soon were sitting at empty tables while the new Oriental raked in the money. Many of these disgruntled owners and gamblers moved to disrupt the heavy business at the Oriental. In the forefront of this move was Johnny Tyler, who had a reputation as a pistoleer. Night after night, Tyler began to intimidate the Oriental's customers. None of the three owners of the Oriental were gunfighters, and they desperately needed someone to put an end to this disruption. They offered Wyatt Earp a quarter interest in the business, if he would take care of Tyler, and keep things running smoothly at the Oriental.

Wyatt accepted the offer, knowing the quarter interest would be a gold mine. Earp promptly slapped the self-styled gunman, threw him out into the street, and told him to leave town. Wyatt's shadow, Doc Holliday, immediately tried to crowd Tyler into a gunfight and humiliated him even more. Tyler left town like a whipped dog.

When Mike Joyce saw what a gold mine the partners had made out of the Oriental, he was immediately sorry he had leased it to them, for he could have gotten a professional gambler to manage it for him, and had the enormous profit himself. Immediately Joyce began to plan on how he could slow the flow of money at the Oriental, and force them to abandon the lease. He knew his political cohort, Sheriff Johnny Behan, could be counted upon to egg the "cowboys" into continuing to disrupt the play in gambling hall. Wyatt Earp was then deputy sheriff of Pima County, as well as employed by Wells Fargo. He had his duties to perform, and he knew he couldn't always be around to keep the cowboy faction from making trouble. When everything was running smoothly at the Oriental, Wyatt was making a lot of money with his share of the profits. He knew he needed someone working inside, someone with a reputation whom the trouble makers wouldn't dare fool with. Better yet, two men would be ideal, top rank gamblers who would bring in more money for the house—and who could be counted on to handle any trouble that might came their way. Wyatt knew whom the two men would be—if he could get them.

Wyatt talked to his partners, and told them he wanted to bring Luke Short and Bat Masterson to deal at the Oriental. He added it wasn't likely there would be any trouble with those two running the games.

Luke had worked for Bill Harris in Dodge, and Dick Clark was good friends with both men. They immediately agreed.

"We'll have to pay them well," Wyatt said.

"Of course," Bill Harris agreed. "Let's offer them twenty-five dollars for a six hour shift, with five dollars an hour for overtime. We're making good money and it'll be worth it to have men of that caliber."

That night Wyatt sent a wire to Luke in Leadville, Colorado, with his offer, adding trouble was brewing in Tombstone and he needed help. Bat Masterson had been living in Kansas City, but Wyatt caught him in Dodge in December, and sent him the same request as he had Luke.

Luke had been freelance gambling in Leadville, with side trips to Denver, Cheyenne and Deadwood, so he was free to pack up immediately. He had been hearing stories from Tombstone, and was anxious to see it himself. Around the latter part of 1880, he took a train south to Trinidad, Colorado, where he changed trains and went on into Santa Fe, New Mexico on the Santa Fe Railroad to the end of the line. From the rail end, he took a stage coach to Deming, New Mexico, where the Southern Pacific was building its lines east toward El Paso. From Deming, he rode a Southern Pacific work train to Benson, Arizona, and then the Wells Fargo stagecoach along the San Pedro River toward Tombstone. The population of Tombstone was around seventy-five hundred by the time Luke arrived, and growing every day. Wages at the mines were good, and even the laborers had plenty of money to spend.

In Tombstone Luke got a room at the Cosmopolitan Hotel, which was the Earp brothers headquarters, and then walked over to the Oriental on the corner of Allen and Fifth Streets.

Dick Clark and Bill Harris greeted Luke and began to introduce Lou Rickenbaugh; Luke remembered meeting the high rolling gambler before in Kansas City.

That evening, when Wyatt Earp walked back into the gambling hall, he found Luke seated behind the faro layout dealing. A grin touched Wyatt's lips as he shook hands. "They got you working already?"

"After sitting on bouncing stages, this chair feels pretty good," Luke said.

Wyatt brought Luke up to date on the state of affairs between the Behan—Joyce faction and the cowboys supporting them. "Bat's coming, too. Should be here in a week or two."

Bat Masterson arrived in Tombstone by the same route as Luke, sometime after the middle of February, 1881. He was happy to meet all of his old friends at the Oriental again, and after getting settled in at the hotel where Luke was staying, he began working at the Oriental with Luke. Bat hadn't been there much more than a week when trouble broke out, not with local cowboys, but between Luke and gambler Charlie Storms.

Charlie Storms had been born in New Orleans somewhere in the middle 1820's. He had gone into gambling early, learning most of it from a crooked riverboat gambler. In the early 1850's he had gone to California and made a fortune working a crooked faro box. Later he went back to the States and blew it all in a big, long, debauchery. About the time the railroads were moving west, Charlie, broke, showed up at the hell-on-wheels towns which sprang up to separate the railroad workers from their money. Mention any one of the towns: Ogallala, Sidney, Julesberg, or Cheyenne, and Storms had been there. Storms had also gambled in Deadwood, Denver, and Leadville. In the middle 1870's Storms now wanted to be taken as an honest gambler, and accorded the status that went with it, but there were many who said, "once a crooked dealer—always a crooked dealer."[3]

Luke Short had never liked the man, nor trusted him. They had had a run-in in Cheyenne over a card game. Later, in Deadwood, Storms' animosity had known no bounds when a handsome widow had spurned his advances and become involved with Luke.

When Charlie Storms showed up in booming Tombstone, he was fifty-seven years of age and getting grey, but had lost none of his nastiness. He had been involved in many quarrels and gunfights, and had a fearsome reputation. Wyatt Earp later classed him as one of the most dangerous gunfighters around the Cheyenne-Deadwood-Sidney area. It was rumored he had killed five or six men in duels. Charlie Storms was a generation older than many of the boomers in Tombstone, but his temper and his ability to handle liquor hadn't improved with age.

The night of February 24, Storms spent gambling and drinking at one gambling house or another. He had a bad run of luck and lost quite a bit of money.

Early the next morning he showed up at the Oriental, and found Luke Short still dealing faro. Charlie put down several bets, and lost. He began cursing, and started moving bets after Luke called, "All bets down, gentlemen!"

Luke pointedly warned Storms about fooling with the bets,

and Charlie began cursing him. Some witnesses claimed Storms slapped Luke with his gloves, others say he threw his chips in Luke face. In any event, Bat Masterson, standing near Storms, saw both men beginning to draw. As the other players dove for cover, Masterson grabbed Storms' gun hand, and put his body between Storms and Luke.

"Don't shoot, Luke!" Bat begged.

While Luke held his fire, his face white with anger, Bat, who'd been friendly with Storms in Colorado, and in Cheyenne and Deadwood, put Storms' pistol in his belt and, with an arm around Storms, walked him outside.

It was a cool morning in Tombstone, with a brisk February breeze coming from the southwest. Bat stopped on the boardwalk in front of the Oriental and tried to calm Storms down.

"He was threatening me, Bat!" Storms raged.

"He *wasn't* threatening you! I saw it all! He asked you to leave your bets alone after the call!"

"I'll kill him!" Storm said.

Bat looked at Storms in exasperation. "You fool with Luke, and he'll put you down for good. I know him!"

"That'll be the day!"

Bat just shook his head in exasperation; he knew Storms had been drinking all night and there was no use trying to reason with him.

"You're underestimating Luke, Charlie. Let's go back to your hotel room, you've been up all night. Get some rest."

"I'll—"

Bat put a hand on Charlie's shoulder, and said patiently, "We're friends, aren't we, Charlie?"

Storms nodded.

"Do me a favor. Let's go back to your room. If you've got a grievance we can talk about it later. For now, get some rest. All right?"

Storms nodded, and Masterson walked him down the street, his hand still on his shoulder, and took him into the San Jose House, at the corner of Fremont and Fifth Streets where he had a room.

Masterson got Storms into his room and sitting on the bed. He pulled off Storms' boots, and prepared to leave. "You all right now, Charlie?"

Storms nodded, and lay back on the bed. Masterson began to leave, and Storms said, "Where's my pistol?"

Masterson took it from his waistband and put it on the top of the dresser. "See you later, Charlie."

Back on Allen Street, Masterson walked back to the Oriental Saloon. Luke was standing on the sidewalk smoking. He had on his gambler's face, but it was white, and beneath it, Masterson knew he was furious.

"Look, Luke," Masterson pleaded, "Charlie's not really so bad . . . he's just been drinking . . . "

"Storms is a meanspirited son of a bitch!" Luke said. "And a crooked gambler besides; I have no use for him!"

"Luke, he's a friend of mine from Cheyenne and Deadwood! Let it go for now! Let him get some rest! I'm asking you as a friend."

Luke turned and looked up Allen Street towards the east. The sun was just rising behind the Dragoon Mountains. "All right," he said finally.

The stocky Masterson turned and put a hand on Luke's shoulder. "I appreciate it, Luke," he said.

At that moment Luke was grabbed from behind and spun around. Charlie Storms had him by the arm pulling him off the boardwalk. Storms cursed Luke, and began drawing his revolver.

Luke's hand had been near his hip pocket, and he drew his snub-nosed .45 and placed it almost against Storms' heart and pulled the trigger. The tremendous blast of the black powder and the .45 caliber bullet blew Storms backward, slamming into his heart and set his shirt on fire. Luke shot him once more as he went down. Storms was game, as he fell he fired his Colt several times into the boardwalk, but very likely it was only reflex, for he was a dead man.

Luke stood there a moment looking down at Storms, his wool shirt still burning, then rotated the cylinder of his Colt and reloaded from cartridges in one of his vest pockets. He slipped the Colt back into his special hip holster, and turned to the stunned Masterson.[4]

"You sure as hell pick some of the damnedest people for friends, Bat!" He said. He was referring to Ben Thompson and his uncontrollable younger brother, Billy, as well as Bat's late friend, Charlie Storms.[5] Luke brushed some of the burnt black powder residue from the sleeve of his white shirt, then turned and went back into the Oriental, leaving Masterson and a few silent bystanders to deal with the dead Storms.

Back in the Oriental's washroom, Luke took off his vest and washed his hands and face, then brushed the sleeves of his shirt. He put his vest back on, then went out into the gaming room and took over his faro table from the dealer who had filled in for him.

Meanwhile, a crowd had gathered outside, and City Marshal Ben Sippy arrived. Masterson explained what had happened and, not knowing what else to do, they carried Storms back to his room at the San Jose House. They put him upon his bed until Dr. Goodfellow was found to look at him.

It was sometime later that Marshal Sippy and Masterson came into the Oriental where Luke was calmly dealing faro. At the sight of them, Luke turned the game over to his lookout and went to meet them. The three men went to an empty table in the corner and sat down.

"Are you arresting me?" Luke asked Sippy.

The marshal shook his head. "Bat told me what happened,

and I've been aware that Storms was drinking and working himself into a rage most of the night. I've also talked to several men who witnessed the incident out in front. I want you and Bat to come down to the office and give me written statements. I also think it would be wise to get notarized statements from the witnesses. It's clearly a case of self-defense, but we have to go by the rules. Luke, I don't expect you to leave town until all this is settled."

Luke nodded. "Of course."

This is the story Luke later told his brothers Henry and Young; it is basically the same story that Bat Masterson has told.

Several historians have said that Luke was cleared of murder charges in Tucson. There is no evidence of this, but there is an incomplete record in the county courthouse in Bisbee.

This is the entry for May 2, 1881: "Luke Short—defendant—Charge: Murder. F. J. Drum for the Territory. W. J. Hunsacker for the defendant.

May 2, papers filed from Justice Court.

Cost $1.75

July 7, Credit by County Warrant: $1.75

Disposition of Case:

Discharged from custody by Justice on examination for murder.

Ignored by Grand Jury."

By his own account, Luke was not lodged in jail, and as the above record shows, the Grand Jury refused to present a true bill against him in the shooting. Indeed, George Parsons, in his diary, states Luke, by all accounts completely unflappable, had returned to his faro game. He had acceded to Masterson's wishes, and put his pistol away inside the Oriental gaming room, but when Storms returned and grabbed him and started to draw, Luke shot him and made sure he wouldn't get up. The man had forced the fight upon Luke, and gotten himself killed. It was that simple.

If Luke was considered a man to be left alone before the Storms affair, he immediately was elevated to a position of awe by many of the citizens of Tombstone. His coolness during the shooting, then returning to his faro game, surely impressed his friends and enemies alike. If the critics said Storms had been drinking and might have been slow getting his gun out, the fact remains Storms had been drinking when he'd killed most of his other victims, and was considered one of the most dangerous men in the west.

Indeed, for more than a hundred years writers have somehow implied that Luke was lucky in his gunfight with Storms, as well as the subsequent duel with Longhaired Jim Courtright, in Fort Worth, Texas. The fact of the matter is, he was always cool and completely unflappable in any dangerous situation, or he wouldn't have lived through the Indian attacks as a boy, or the attack of the five Sioux while riding dispatches for Crook and Thornburgh. Then there were the two men he'd killed while trading with T. J. near the Red Cloud and Spotted Tail agencies in Nebraska. Although Luke never claimed to be a gunfighter, he already had at this time more real experience in gunfights than friends Bat Masterson and Wyatt Earp together.[6] In all this one thing stands out: Luke Short had the ability to analyze a situation in a instant, then act in his best interest.

Luke and Bat Masterson had no real trouble after the Storms' affair, though on March 1, One-armed Kelly was shot in the Oriental by a man named McAllister. Evidently Mike Joyce, the building owner, talked to the partners of the Oriental gambling hall, and they all decided to close down for a few days.

In April Bat Masterson received a wire from his brother,

Jim, back in Dodge City, saying he'd had trouble with Al Updegraff and A. J. Peacock. Peacock and Masterson were partners in a saloon in Dodge, and there was a quarrel between Jim Masterson and Updegraff, their bartender, who was also brother-in-law to Peacock. Peacock sided with Updegraff, and threats were made. Jim Masterson asked Bat to come help him, as he feared for his life.

Bat Masterson left Tombstone and headed for Dodge City. When he arrived and stepped off the train in Dodge, he ran into Peacock and Updegraff, and all three men drew their pistols and began to shoot. Others in town took sides, and soon bullets were flying. Everyone took cover and when the shooting was over, Al Updegraff was the only one wounded with a lung shot, from which he recovered.

Back in Tombstone, things were heating up between the Earps and the Behan—cowboy faction. On the Earp fighting side were: Wyatt, Virgil, Morgan and Warren, with the loyal Doc Holliday always ready to assist Wyatt.

Sheriff Behan and the cowboys were Democrats, and the Earps were Republicans. It was generally thought by the Earps and their backers, of whom many were Tombstone's leaders and businessmen, that Behan was the protector of the outlaw bunch, which included Old Man Clanton, his sons, Billy and Ike, Curly Bill Brocius, the two McLaury brothers, Frank and Tom, Johnny Ringo, Frank Stilwell, Pete Spence, and various others. The Earp faction also believed that Sheriff Behan got a percentage from the outlaw's activities. Behan also had business interests in Tombstone; he and John Dunbar were partners in the Dexter Livery Stable. Behan and Mike Joyce, who owned the Oriental building, were fellow Democrats and close friends. When Behan and Joyce saw the gambling concession at the Oriental was so lucrative, Behan had encouraged the cowboys to disrupt the business, in the hope the gambling house partners would lose business and abandon their lease with Joyce.

With Luke and Masterson to keep out the trouble makers, Behan and Joyce were frustrated. There was no way to get Clark, Harris, Rickenbaugh and Earp out of the building until the lease was up, but Behan could cause them trouble, and he used the animosity between the cowboys and the Earps to do this.

On March 16, there was an attempted robbery of the Kinnear stage about eight miles north of Contention. Bud Philpot was driving and Bob Paul was riding shotgun. There was $25,000 in silver aboard the stage. In the exchange of gunfire, Philpot was shot through the heart and a passenger, Peter Roerig, was mortally wounded. This crime really crystallized the enmity between the Earp faction and the so-called cowboys.

The manhunt following the stage robbery finally netted Luther King, who implicated others in the cowboy—rustler gang. King was placed in the Tombstone jail, but somehow "escaped." Many Tombstone residents believed it was a well-planned job to get King away. The Earps naturally suspected the work of Sheriff Johnny Behan.

Luke Short had been watching all the tensions building into a real feud. He knew as soon as one of the principals on either side was killed, it would develop into a bloody war. He knew there was no reason for him to remain in Tombstone and get involved in such a feud. Wyatt had three brothers and the redoubtable Doc Holliday to back him up; friends like Texas Jack Vermilion, Sherman McMasters, and Turkey Creek Jack Johnson, gunfighters all, could be called if the Earps needed more help. Besides, after killing Storms, the fun had gone out of Tombstone for Luke. He had never started a fight in his life, and he detested the fact that a gambler had to protect his game with a pistol. Moreover, he had standing offers in Leadville and Denver to deal for more money than he was making in Tombstone. One day he spoke his thoughts of leaving Tombstone to his friend, Bill Harris. Harris, too, could see a bloody fight coming between the two factions in Tombstone, and had already decided to sell his interest in the Oriental to either Dick Clark or to Lou Rickerbaugh. As soon as the deal was concluded, he was going back to Dodge City, where he not only still owned half interest in the profitable Long Branch Saloon, but also had a sizeable cattle operation with Chalk Beeson. Beyond that, he was interested in starting a bank in Dodge. He urged Luke to come with him and again take over the management of the Long Branch's gambling concession.

Luke thanked Harris, but declined, telling him he wanted to go back to Colorado for awhile. "As soon as this murder charge of Storms is cleared up, I'm leaving." Luke said. "Jesus, Bill, I hate this damn business of having to wear a pistol and shoot it out with some drunken gunman! I'm a professional gambler—not a gunfighter!"

Harris laughed. "Well, my friend, you are looked upon as one now. Good luck!"

Shortly thereafter Bill Harris finalized the selling of his share of the Oriental's gambling business to his principal partners, and left Tombstone, headed east for Kansas. What Harris and Luke both sensed, was that the big money in Tombstone had peaked, and was on the way down. Luke knew Leadville was a much better prospect in the long term.

Luke continued to deal faro at the Oriental, waiting for the Grand Jury to rule on the murder charge against him. He was at loose ends, and often when his shift was over went up or down the street to buck the tiger. While he was waiting he had an incredible run of luck at the competition's faro tables. By July 7th, when the Grand Jury refused to bring a true bill against him in the death of Charlie Storms, he had taken several thousand dollars from the Crystal Palace, the

159

Alhambra, Occidental, and others.

Luke had already talked to his employers, telling them he was going back to Colorado if charges against him were dropped, and so, sometime around the middle of July, he packed his trunk and made ready to leave Tombstone.

He left town on a beautiful summer day. The monsoon rains had saturated the desert and the grass was green and all manner of wild flowers colored the land. Even the mesquite, catclaw and ocotillo looked happy with the recent rains. Luke gazed from the open stagecoach window as the coach swept down Fremont Street, made the turn north, then rolled past the graveyard where the irascible Charlie Storms lay in his grave beneath a heap of boulders. Luke knew there would be a lot more boulder heaped graves when the Earp-Behan/Cowboys feud accelerated.

The stagecoach rolled north, roughly following the San Pedro River toward the rail-town of Benson. This would be a much easier trip than the one when he had come to Tombstone eight months earlier. The Southern Pacific Railroad had finished the last stretch back in March, and now it was possible to ride all the way to Colorado or Kansas City by train. Luke planned to transfer in El Paso to the Atchison, Topeka and Sante Fe, and ride on into Colorado. From Trinidad he could catch the Denver and Rio Grande.

* * *

In Tombstone, the battle was just beginning. Around the time Short and Harris left, Old Man Clanton and his sons, Ike and Billy, Tom and Frank McLaury, Charlie Snow, John Ringo and others were believed to have waylaid and killed eight Mexican smugglers in Skeleton Canyon, and made off with $4,000 in coin, silver bullion, some mescal and quite a bunch of livestock.

One of the Mexican smugglers had escaped the cowboys, however, and a month later the family got sweet revenge. They ambushed the outlaws in Guadalupe Canyon, and killed Old Man Clanton, Charlie Snow, Dick Gray and Jim Crane in the first volley of rifle fire. Bill Long died of his wounds later. Bill Byers and Harry Ernshaw escaped. The cowboy-rustlers were being cut down.

On October 27, 1881, Wyatt, Virgil and Morgan Earp, with Doc Holliday, shot it out with the two McLaury brothers and Ike and Billy Clanton near the O. K. Corral. Ike Clanton, the one who instigated the fight with his big mouth and threats against the Earps, cut and ran, and left his younger brother Billy, and the McLaurys dead on the ground.

Virgil Earp was ambushed and shot as he crossed Fifth Street on December twenty-third by two or three men. Virgil lived, but his left arm was crippled and he was wounded also in his upper thigh. About four or five inches of badly shattered bone in his left arm had to be removed and he was never able to use the arm again. It was a cowardly ambush generally thought to be the work of Ike Clanton, Frank Stilwell, Hank Swilling and perhaps John Ringo.

The lawlessness prompted former Governor Anson Safford to send U. S. Marshal Crawley Dake to Tombstone to check on the situation. Acting Governor John Gosper invested Wyatt Earp with complete powers of U.S. Marshall, and appointed under him, deputies Morgan and Warren Earp, Doc Holliday, Sherman McMasters, Texas Jack Vermillion, and Turkey Creek Jack Johnson. With this authority, they began to hunt the cowboys who had ambushed Virgil in earnest.

In between all this came the end of the year, and the lease on the gambling room in the Oriental was up. Being realistic, the three remaining partners, Lou Rickenbaugh, Dick Clark, and Wyatt Earp, doubted that Mike Joyce would renew the lease on the lucrative property. On January first, bright and early, Mike Joyce predictably informed the partners he wouldn't be renewing their lease. They stripped the gaming room of everything they had added, all the beautiful inlaid hardwood gaming tables, chairs, the crystal chandeliers, even the elegant Brussels carpet that covered the floor.

"Good luck," Wyatt told the grinning Mike Joyce.

Their spies told the partners Joyce had already ordered new tables and chandeliers and carpet from Sam Francisco and as soon as it all arrived and was installed, Joyce opened. Also installed, as manager of the gambling house, was none other than Sheriff John Behan, no surprise either to the partners, who had leased another building and were back in business.

But the show wasn't over. Dick Clark and Wyatt Earp were waiting to settle some scores with the wily Behan. The day of the grand reopening of the Oriental gaming room, the two partners went to buck the Oriental's Tiger. Their spies had informed them Behan had only $5,000 in his bank. They took seats at the faro table which was run by a dealer named Fries. Just having Earp across from the table intimidated Fries, and his nervousness clearly showed. The other players clearly saw a battle was in the works, and dropped out. John Behan watched Wyatt buy $1,000 worth of chips, and moved in to take over the lookout's chair. Dick Clark took over the casekeeper's position, operating the abacuslike device that showed which cards had been played in a set. The play went back and forth for an hour, neither side showing an advantage, until Wyatt won twice in a row. Sensing he was on a roll, he bet $1,000, and won and won and won. When he had $6,000 in chips in front of him, he stood up and told the nervous dealer to cash him out.

"Wha—what's the problem?" stammered John Behan.

"No problem," Wyatt said, "I'm just quitting while I'm ahead." He shoved the chips across the table toward Behan.

Behan just stared at him in shock.

"Look," Wyatt said, "I put $1,000 into your cash drawer—and you only had $5,000 to start with. Why should I play against my own money?"

"I'm good for anything you win!" Behan blustered.

"I doubt that, Johnny," Wyatt said, looking him straight in the eye. "Didn't you hear me—I said cash me out!"

Behan was humiliated in front of the crowd which had gathered around the faro table to watch the play. He had to go to every table in the room to make up the $6,000 he owed Wyatt.[7]

The tall, elegant Dick Clark met Wyatt's eyes as they waited for Behan to collect the money. No expression touched either man's poker face, but their eyes did the smiling.

The Behan-Joyce bank was broke, and Behan had to close the gaming room while he looked for financial backing. His attempt to make it big in the Oriental never really succeeded at all, and it was one more thing he hated Wyatt Earp for. The first thing was that Wyatt had stolen the affections of Behan's girlfriend, the beautiful Josie from San Francisco, and she now lived with Wyatt.

Before leaving the gambling hall, Wyatt counted out $3,000 in front of Behan, and handed it to his partner, Dick Clark. The two men then walked out into the saloon part, and ordered drinks for the house.

"Ah, friend, Dick," Wyatt said raising his glass, "revenge is sweet, *verdad*?"

"*Si*," Clark replied in Spanish. "Indeed, so!"

* * *

But there was more tragedy for the Earps. On Sunday, March 19, 1882, assassins shot through a window and killed

Morgan Earp while he played pool in Campbell and Hatch's saloon. Morgan lived only about forty minutes. It was thought Frank Stilwell, Pete Spence, Fritz Bode and Indian Charley were the men involved in Morgan's murder.

The following day Morgan Earp's body was taken to Contention City and put on the train that would take it to Colton, California, where the Earps' parents lived. Crippled Virgil Earp was still in great pain, but he and his wife, along with Morgan's grieving widow, accompanied the body. Wyatt, brother Warren, Doc Holliday, Sherman McMasters, and Jack Johnson went as guards as far as Tucson.

Wyatt, Warren, and Doc Holliday spied the skulking Frank Stilwell and Ike Clanton around the train station in Tucson and went after them. Ike Clanton escaped, but when the train pulled out, Frank Stilwell was found dead with shotgun and bullet wounds.

A grand jury issued an indictment against Wyatt and Warren Earp, Holliday, Sherman McMasters, and Jack Johnson, but by the time Stilwell's body was discovered, the men had already returned to Tombstone.

Informed of Stilwell's killing, Sheriff Behan tried to arrest Wyatt and his friends, but Wyatt just looked at him with his steely grey eyes, and said, "Just try it, Johnny." When Sheriff Behan didn't do anything, Wyatt contemptuously turned his back to him, mounted up, and with Brother Warren and his friends, rode out of Tombstone.

On March 22, the Earp party killed Florentino Cruz at Pete Spense's wood camp in South Pass of the Dragoon Mountains, and on March 24, Wyatt Earp killed Curly Bill Brocius with a shotgun at Mescal Springs, between the Whetstone and Mustang Mountains.[8]

They couldn't bring Morgan back from the dead, nor restore Virgil's crippled arm, but they had sent some of culprits to the grave where they'd do no more harm. They made one last sweep around the area, hoping to find Ike Clanton or Pete Spence, among others, but Ike Clanton had probably followed the other outlaws across the border to Mexico. Pete Spence, not too brave either, rode into Tombstone and Sheriff Behan gave him sanctuary in the jail. Behan turned him loose a few days later, after Spence decided it was safe to travel.

Wyatt and his party, unable to find any more of the cowboys, knew they would have little chance of beating the warrants against them for Stillwell's death in court, especially with John Behan still Sheriff, and they rode on to Silver City, New Mexico, sold their horses and proceeded on to Colorado by stagecoach and train.

It was a saddened Wyatt Earp who went to Colorado to hide out. As time went on he began to see that his fight with Sheriff Behan and the cowboys was destined to fail. Several years later, in Dodge he said to Luke, "If not for my pride I'd have led my brothers away from Tombstone, and Morg would be alive, and Virg whole."

There is no doubt that for the rest of his life he was plagued by that "if."

CHAPTER EIGHTEEN

There were more than 45,000 people crammed into Leadville and the gulches surrounding the town by the time Luke Short returned. The payroll was almost $1,000,000 a month, and the good life was there; all you needed was the money to pursue it.

The elegant Clarendon and the Hotel Vendome were full. In the fashionable stores you could buy anything from silk stockings to diamonds, the latest French gowns, and caviar and champagne. There were churches and schools, as well as three daily newspapers.

For the miners with money to spend, and the wealthy mine owners and businessmen, there were more than 120 gambling halls, about the same number of saloons, and enough bordellos to take care of all those so inclined. The girls ranged from two dollar cribbers to high-priced prostitutes for the well-heeled. Amusements of any variety were available such as lady wrestlers in some of the lower class joints, tattoo parlors, cockfights and bear wrestling shows, strong men and strong women acts, fortunetellers, and opium parlors. For more classy entertainment there was the Tabor Opera House, built by the Silver King himself, or the Grand Central Theater where very talented singers, musicians and actors gave shows rivaling New York, or even Paris. French chefs dominated the dining rooms of the top eateries, and oysters, mountain quail and caviar were on the menu. One fancy restaurant brought in glacier ice over two thousand years old, and a clever ice sculptor created works of art to grace the tables of the rich party givers. The ice was pulled from the sea off the face of glaciers in Alaska by the steam winches aboard huge sailing ships, stowed in their holds, then run south to San Francisco and unloaded into insulated railroad cars. It was then shipped to Leadville, where the white coated bartenders used the age-old ice in their drinks to the delight of the customers, who would ooh-and-ahh as the compressed air bubbles trapped inside the ice exploded like gunshots. The aged glacier ice was slow to melt and was preferred over any other. Soon the competing restaurants had to have glacier ice, too, and it was demanded in Denver, as well.

Luke found a comfortable room and settled in to gamble at some of the classier gambling establishments. One night he met H. A. W. Tabor in the Saddle Rock Cafe. Tabor, now a multi-millionaire, and getting richer by the day, insisted Luke move to his table. Luke had all ready won a considerable amount of money from Tabor, and now he wanted a chance to get even.

The stories of Tabor's gambling were legendary. On one occasion Tabor was in a game with a well-heeled merchant on a train, and was winning with high stakes. Finally the merchant drew a powerful hand—four kings. He bet all his remaining money and all his jewelry on the hand. He then asked Tabor if he could write an additional $2,000 check to raise the pot. Tabor studied his hand, then hummed to himself, as if he were undecided. "Okay," he finally said, "providing I can draw a queen from the discards."

The merchant checked his hand again, and tried to think how a queen would give Tabor the edge. There was no way a queen could beat him. "All right," he agreed, then asked if he could increase the bet to $3,000.

Tabor nodded, and the man tossed his check into the huge pot, then gleefully laid down the four kings. His glee quickly left him when Tabor put down his hand; four aces—and the lone queen. The merchant was stunned and quickly got up from the table and left.

Sometime later he came into the bar where Tabor was having a drink, and smoking a cigar. "Pardon me, Senator," the merchant asked, "could you please tell me what you wanted that queen for?"

At the question, the poker faced Tabor broke up completely in laughter.[1]

Tabor was a good poker player, but a top professional like Luke, always had the edge. Luke fattened his purse with Tabor that night, and Tabor insisted they have an early morning breakfast together at the Saddle Rock Cafe. Tabor enjoyed his gambling, win or lose, for there was always more money from his mines.

It was about this time Tabor had shipped his protesting wife to Denver and built an Italian villa for her and his son. Augusta had taken to the millionaire status no better than the two Germans, Hook and Rische. She worried about the way Tabor was spending money, and objected to his gambling and late night parties. Finally, Tabor gave up trying to get her to enjoy the millions they had, and began to enjoy the party life with dance hall girls and entertainers. Now, Tabor was in a fine mood, for he had just met the voluptuous young divorcee, Baby Doe, who was to be his companion and wife for the rest of his life.

Luke turned down several chances to deal faro at various gambling halls, and continued to free-lance. One day he received a wire from Bill Harris in Dodge City. Bill said that he and Chalk Beeson would like Luke to come to Dodge and manage the gambling at the Long Branch. Harris also said he was sure Beeson might be in the mood to sell his half of the business in the future.

Luke liked the idea of a share in the Long Branch and the next morning wired acceptance to Harris and had his traveling trunks put on the train.

As Luke rode east, he reflected on the changes in the country over the past few years. Now, you could ride all the way from New York to San Francisco in a Pullman. Then, if you so desired, catch the Southern Pacific south across southern Arizona Territory, New Mexico, through Kansas to Kansas City, and make many connections in towns in between. All the railroad towns had telegraph offices, and regular telegraph offices in the cities kept track of the stock markets, and fed news to the newspapers.

Luke thought about how you could ride almost anywhere in the West without worrying about the Indians lifting your hair. Little Wolf and Dull Knife's breakout from Indian Territory three years before was about the last bloody fight.

Oh, there had been the Ute rebellion when his friend, Major Thornburgh, had been sacrificed by the overbearing actions of the Indian agent, Meeker. Poor, gallant Thornburgh, dead on the banks of the Milk River.[2] Chief Joseph was defeated and on a reservation as were both Spotted Tail and Red Cloud. Crazy Horse had been killed after his arrest. Sitting Bull was back from hiding out in Canada, and rumor had it he would join Buffalo Bill and his Wild West Show. About the only wild Indians left were Geronimo and his followers who were again leading General Crook all over southern Arizona Territory and raiding and hiding out in Old Mexico.

Settlers were safe in little isolated settlements all over the West and more were coming every day.

As the train rolled on Luke considered the job of managing the Long Branch again. It could work out pretty well. And if Beeson did decide to sell Luke his half of the business, he had the money saved up to bank the games. After all the years of hard work, he might actually be able to have a business of his own. The thought made him feel really good. You just couldn't try to bank a game with a few thousand dollars. John Behan had lost his bank in Tombstone in a little more than two hours, when Wyatt Earp and Dick Clark had gone after him.

Luke arrived in Dodge City sometime in late August, 1881. He settled into his favorite corner room at the Great Western House with his friends, the Gallands.

Though it was now August, the trail herds had been pouring into Dodge since spring, and would keep on coming until October or November.

Luke soon had his dealers sorted out. He let one man go and replaced him with a man he knew in Kansas City.

Many of the herd owners would take their whole family across Texas to New Orleans, then board a riverboat steamer and proceed north to St. Louis where they could catch the Atchison, Topeka and Sante Fe on to Dodge. It wouldn't be long before they would be able to ride the train from Fort Worth to Dodge.

The owners, some very wealthy barons from previous cattle sales, would lodge their families in the Dodge House, or the Great Western Hotel, and wait for their herds to come north to the Arkansas River. Almost 400,000 longhorns had been driven up to Kansas the previous year, and a good percentage had come to Dodge to be sold. The figures for 1881 might be down a bit so far, but the price of cattle had risen, and there was more money than ever circulating in town.

Luke's share since he had taken over the management of the gaming tables was substantial. Part of the huge success of the Long Branch was because the herd owners and trail bosses and cowboys, who flocked to the saloon and gambling tables, knew Luke or knew of him, and trusted him. In all the years he'd gambled, he'd always had the name as an honest dealer.

When the cattle season was over, Luke went East on a trip, stopping over in Kansas City to visit with many of his friends, and to buck someone else's tiger. From there he went on to Chicago and New York, where he had a tailor make him several custom-made suits and top coats. One thing Luke never seemed to have enough of was clothes. He also saw all the stage shows and vaudeville acts, and bought many books at the bookstores. Luke was a very private sort of man. There was no braggadocio about him and he never mentioned anything about the many women he'd known. As he lay dying, he kept quiet about this part of his life when he spoke to his brothers. Young and Henry believed that on this trip to New York, he met and became seriously smitten with the petite, blond woman who had the same name as his mother, Hettie, and married her.[3]

Luke evidently didn't want to bring Hettie to Dodge when he returned west just before the first trail herds began to arrive the next spring. Dodge was still a rough town, and perhaps he couldn't find an adequate place for her to stay.

The 1882 cattle season was again a good one, and as the Texans returned home, Luke went back to New York to be with Hettie. He didn't stay long, for Bill Harris wired him to come back to Dodge. Chalk Beeson was finally ready to sell his half of the Long Branch business to Luke.

In February of 1883, the deal was concluded. Beeson still owned the building itself, but Luke Short and Bill Harris were now equal owners in the business. For the first time Luke had a piece of the business he loved, and it was no run-of-the-mill saloon; it was the renowned Long Branch Saloon and Gambling House.

Many changes were to come in Dodge City in the spring of 1883. First, Chalk Beeson bought Alonzo Webster's Stock Exchange Saloon next door, and Webster moved to the corner of the block and took over the management of the Old House Saloon. He already owned the building, but now took over the management himself. Perhaps he wanted to distance himself from the Long Branch, for the Texans avoided him because he was a northerner and filled the popular Long Branch to overflowing. It had hurt him badly financially and no doubt was the cause of the fight to come.

Luke wasn't aware of it at the time, but forces were moving inexorably toward a serious confrontation much like the one between the Earps and Sheriff Behan back in Tombstone. Again, the issues would be money.

Bill Harris and Chalk Beeson had been partners in the Saratoga Saloon before buying the Long Branch, as well as partners in a sizable cattle operation. Their cattle brand was COD. Harris was also one of the organizers of Dodge City's first bank, and was an officer of it, as well as owning a quarter share of the stock in the bank. He was a well-known Dodge City businessman, and a resident for some years. Many of his friends and other businessmen and persuaded him to run for the office of mayor.

The previous mayor had been none other than Harris and Short's competitor, Alonzo Webster. Webster had campaigned for law and order. There was nothing wrong with this, in fact, it was laudable, but from records and newspapers of the era, it looks as if Webster simply wanted to get rid of his competition. To put himself into that position of power, immediately following Bill Harris' declaration to run for mayor, Webster proposed his crony, Larry Deger, to oppose Harris. Deger was a 300 pound German-American, almost porcine in appearance, who had beaten Bat Masterson in the election for sheriff back in 1877. James (Dog) Kelley had fired Deger from the job, and now Deger had been working for a freight company.

Webster and Deger ran a dirty campaign from the start,

calling Bill Harris a protector of confidence men, thieves, and gamblers. Deger handily won the election, but it stank to Dog Kelley and all the rest of the gang which favored Harris. The "Gang" was a name the Reformers had given to Dog Kelly, Bill Harris, Chalk Beeson, Luke Short, Bat Masterson, Wyatt Earp, Charlie Bassett, Pat Sughrue, and W. F. Petillon, the Clerk of the District Court, among others. The Gang wanted law and order, too, but they knew from experience that when you tried to stifle the Texans' entertainment you could kill off the town. Although there were a few farmers beginning to come to the area, they didn't spend money like the cowboys did.

The cowboys who arrived had been on the trail from two to four months fighting storms, stampedes, swollen rivers, dust and working eighteen hour days. When they finally arrived at Dodge they wanted first to take a bath, get a haircut, then buy new clothing, and be able to drink in the saloons, gamble, dance or go to the whorehouses if they chose.

Mike Sutton, formerly on the side of Wyatt Earp and Bat Masterson and Dog Kelley, had switched sides as soon as he saw the balance of power swinging toward the so-called reformers. On the day of the election, Sutton brought in a bunch of out-of-town railroaders to vote. Sutton was a lawyer for the Santa Fe Railroad, and this was easy for him to do. Deger had the support of most of the German-Americans who lived in Dodge, many of them businessmen, and the reformers easily won the election.

It was true there had been crooked gamblers and thieves in Dodge, but the honest gamblers deplored these people as much as did the reformers, for it gave them a bad reputation. There were also some female entertainers, who worked in the saloons and were prostitutes, but this had always been the case, and probably always would be. The women working in Webster's Old House Saloon behaved in the same manner as the ones working in the Long Branch, or any other saloon or dancehall. That was what the Texans wanted, and that was what they paid for.

The previous governor of Kansas had been a prohibitionist and had tried to suppress everything the Texas cowboys yearned to do, however, the realists in Dodge knew it was folly to go that route, for they knew what had happened to similar cattle trail towns when this had been tried. They promptly died. Moreover, the license fees and taxes the saloons, gamblers, dance halls, and even the fines the prostitutes paid, were almost twice the amount the other businessmen paid. It was that simple—vice kept the town running. It was, the Gang knew, hypocrisy for the Reformers to take their money on one hand, then denounce them on the other.

Before the Gang could get all the evidence showing that Sutton had really brought in non-residents to vote, and ask for a new election, the mayor-elect swung into action, undoubtedly prompted by the man behind it all—Alonzo Webster, owner of the Old House Saloon.

Mayor Deger and the City Council immediately passed a new city ordinance calling for "the suppression of Vice and Immorality within the City of Dodge City." It went on to proscribe fines against "any person, or persons who shall keep or maintain in this city, a brothel, bawdy house, house of ill fame, or of assignations." There was much more to the ordinance, but that last word in the sentence, said it all, *assignations*. A saloon, gambling house, or dancehall, could be called a "house of assignations" if it was so perceived by the city.[4]

For many years piano and bands and singers were featured in the Long Branch. Chalk Beeson was a talented musician and often had his own band there. After Beeson sold his interest to Luke, he moved his band to his new place of business, the Stock Exchange Saloon. Luke immediately hired a three piece band, as well as three attractive female singers from Kansas City. His good friend, Joe Bassett, who owned the Marble Hall there, had found the singers for Luke. The exuberant cowboys fresh off the Texas trail, found the girls irresistible. If the girls did business with the cowboys on the side, that was none of his concern, Luke thought.

On the evening of February 28, 1883, Luke's singers were arrested by Louis Hartman, the Clerk of the City Court. Hartman had been made a special policeman by City Marshal, Jack Bridges. Luke had been away having supper when the arrests were made. As soon as he was alerted to the situation, he went to the jail to pay their fines and have them released. Hartman told him they couldn't be released as they were being held on charges of prostitution. Luke was white with rage. He immediately went down the street and woke the City Attorney, routing him from his bed with the barrel of his pistol. Bill Harris had also showed up at City Hall, and Luke left Harris with the attorney and went back down Front Street to see if the other saloons had also been raided. He stepped into Webster's Old House Saloon and watched as two girls sang away. A single woman sang also at Heinz and Kramer's Lone Star Saloon, and two more girls were performing at Nelson Cary's Lady Gay Dance Hall. Needless to say, Luke was savage. Only he and another saloon owner had been raided. All of the Reformers' cronies' saloons were going strong.

It was dark now, and only the dim street lights showed the way. As Luke came back down Front Street, he ran into Louis Hartman. Perhaps Luke's killing of Storms in Tombstone unnerved Hartman. In any event, he pulled his pistol and shot at Luke. Luke immediately drew and fired back at Hartman. Hartman fell and Luke thought he had killed him. He immediately went into a friend's saloon, thought it over, then decided to go back to the closed-up Long Branch, and better arm himself, for he could see Webster and Deger's whole scheme now. He left and went to the Long Branch, locked the door behind him, then sat down with a double-barreled shotgun and two loaded pistols on the table before him.

Luke was unaware he hadn't hit Hartman at all in the darkness. Hartman, in his excitement, had simply tripped and fallen. Fearful that Luke's next shots wouldn't miss, he had crawled silently away.

Sometime later Bill Harris came back to the Long Branch and identified himself. Luke let him in. Harris told Luke he hadn't killed Hartman and that Marshal Bridges wanted him to submit to arrest for disturbing the peace. Harris advised him to do so, and simply pay the fine.

With Luke's agreement, Harris went back and got Bridges. When the marshal came, Luke walked back to the jail and was formally arrested. Harris and others of the Gang immediately put up Luke's bail, but he wasn't released. Tom Lane, another saloon owner, who was on Webster and Deger's hit list, was also brought in and arrested, as were several other gamblers, among them "Corn-hole" Johnny Gallager, a young man who was said to have taken to the cards as soon as he could distinguish between the spots.

In the meantime, Webster, Deger, and Tom Nixon, also part owner of the Lady Gay dance hall, had formed a so called "Vigilante" team. Tom Nixon, a former buffalo hunter, was apparently in charge of the vigilantes. Nixon had perhaps 150 armed men who surrounded the jail and prevented Luke and his fellow gamblers from leaving. Finally they were told they had the choice of what train they wanted to get on, the eastbound or the westbound, but that they were leaving Dodge, and they weren't wanted back.

Luke could see there was no use arguing. He chose the eastbound train, and when it stopped he was escorted aboard, without anything but the clothes he wore. He headed for Kansas City where he had many friends and began to work out of a plan.

The Dodge City Saloon War was just beginning.

CHAPTER NINETEEN

In Kansas City Luke found a comfortable place to stay, not far from the Marble Hall. Two years before, when Luke had been there and dealt for Joe Bassett and Colonel Rickets, they had operated their gambling hall over on the Missouri side of the river. Then the Missouri legislature had passed the anti-gambling act, so the partners simply moved across the river to the Kansas side, where gambling was also illegal, but was, in effect, licensed by a periodic fine, the same as it was in Dodge or any other place in Kansas. Both men were close friends of Luke. Luke was welcomed by Joe. He told Joe the whole story of his departure from Dodge.

Joe Bassett just shook his head in disgust. He told Luke to make himself at home, and use the place for his office, while he figured out how to reinstate himself.

Already the newspapers were featuring the story. The papers were either pro-Short or pro-Deger, depending on whom they favored. The *Dodge City Times*, edited by Nick Klaine, naturally lauded the good citizens of Dodge for getting rid of the riff-raff. The *Topeka Daily Capital* took a fairer look at the situation, saying in part:

"Mr. Short is a Texan, who came to Dodge some two years ago, and having been interested in the cattle business—as, indeed, he still is—he had an extensive

178

acquaintance with other cattlemen and their employees. At Dodge he is engaged in the saloon business with a man named Harris, and his friendly relations with the numerous Texans coming to Dodge has made Harris and Short's saloon the most popular and profitable one in the city. Mr. Webster, the late mayor of Dodge, is also a saloon keeper, and during his term of office removed from a more remote location to one next door to Harris and Short's Long Branch, on Front Street.

"While Short's popularity has increased, that gentleman modestly stated, Webster's has declined, and finding it impractical to secure his re-election to the mayority, Webster some weeks before the election brought out Mr. Deger as a candidate, against whom Harris, Short's partner, was nominated. Deger had been a foreman for Lee and Reynolds, who are engaged in freighting and have their place of business outside the city limits. About March 1st, however, it is said, Deger began boarding at a hotel in town, in order to gain a legal residence.

"The night before the election the construction trains of the Sante Fe Railroad, manned by men residing at different places scattered along the line, were run into Dodge, and the next morning the men were all on hand, obtained control of the election board by filling the vacancies under the form of law, and voted.

Thus Deger was elected by a majority . . ."

And so it went. Chicago and New York papers began to follow the story, and things began to heat up. Bat Masterson was in Silverton, Colorado, and Luke decided to go see if he had any advice for reinstating himself. Bat suggested he go see the Governor of Kansas personally and lay out the true story. Governor George Glick was the antiprohibitionist successor to Governor St. John, and Bat thought he would be sympathetic. The Governor had also helped Bat out of a touchy situation in the past. Bat added, if that didn't work, he'd get Wyatt Earp and a few of his friends to come to Dodge if Luke needed muscle. "I'd love to pistol-whip that fat son-of-a-bitch myself!" Bat said of Deger.

Luke went back to Topeka and was granted an interview with Governor Glick. The Governor had read all about the difficulties in Dodge, and asked Luke to lay out the whole story. Luke told him all about it in detail, then added. "Governor, I realize I am at fault to some degree for shooting at City Clerk Hartman, but he fired first, and a man must defend himself. I submitted to arrest, and my friends made my bail. But I was not released and allowed to stand trial; I was summarily and forcibly put aboard the train with several others and told not to come back. I realize a couple of these men, who were evicted along with me, are confidence men or petty crooks, but I am a business man and have long had the reputation of an honest gambler. I think I am entitled to due process of law concerning the charges against me. Also, if I am not permitted to have girls singing or working in the Long Branch, then neither should Webster, Heinz and Kramer, or Nixon and Bond in their saloons and dance halls."

Governor Glick nodded in agreement. "Everything you say makes sense to me—and I don't doubt your word—but do you have someone in Dodge to substantiate what you have just told me?"

Luke told the Governor he would make up a written statement of what he had just related and have it corroborated by W. F. Petillon, Clerk of the District Court of Ford County.

Three days later he delivered the statement to the Governor, with both his and Billy Petillon's notarized signatures.

There is no record of it, but the Governor must have put all this before Deger's new sheriff, George Hinkle, for he soon had a telegram emphatically stating that everything was peaceful in Dodge, there were no mobs or vigilantes, and the City had only expelled a few trouble makers in the interest of peace.

This receipt of Sheriff Hinkle's telegram must have incensed the Governor, for he immediately alerted two companies of the Kansas National Guard, and the commanders wired back they were ready to move on his orders.

Governor Glick sent a long blistering telegram to Sheriff Hinkle, touching upon the expulsion of the men from Dodge for violation of city ordinances, without due process, and of the high-handed way the town was being run. His telegram showed he was not taken in by Hinkle's statement that things were hunky-dory in Dodge, for he already had reports that the train station was guarded by a large number of Deger's men armed with rifles and shotguns who checked out everyone coming to town. He also knew that two gamblers and saloon owner, Tom Lane, had been caught getting off the train, and had been promptly put back aboard at gun point.

The Sheriff was not too bright, for he answered the Governor's telegram with another, stating:

"Mr. Short's expulsion from this city is the direct result of his own actions and the feeling of the people generally is very strong against him."

He went on to list all the prominent men who were behind him. Not once did he address the point the Governor had tried to make in his long, two-page wire: that the men had been railroaded out of town without due process of the law.

The newspapers were eating all this up. D.M. Frost, who published the Ford County Globe, denounced the mob watching the trains arriving in Dodge, and said he had been threatened with death if he didn't keep still. Luke and W. F. Petillon were interviewed by the Topeka Daily Capitol and told their stories again.

The Governor received a telegram from some of the leading businessmen of Dodge, informing him that he had been badly misinformed, and asked him to send the Adjutant General or some other person of power before he acted. The Governor now didn't know what the hell to think. Two of the men, Robert Wright, and G.M. Hoover, were either state representatives, or had held that position.

The newspapers loved it! A reporter caught Luke just after he had come from a meeting with Bat Masterson in Kansas City, and had this to say:

"Mr. Short, who has been observed by many on the streets in Topeka, would hardly meet, in his personal appearance, the expectation of many that have seen or heard him described as a red-handed desperado. He is a man rather under medium height, but well-built and firmly knit, with nothing in his features or complexion to indicate irregular or dissipated habits. He is clean-shaved, excepting for a natty little moustache, and is dressed with great care and in good style. He sports a magnificent diamond pin, and yesterday twirled between his fingers an elegant black walking stick with a gold head. The Capitol knows little of his past history, and can say nothing to the claim of a reputation which has been given him, but there is no doubt he is able to take care of himself in almost any kind of crowd."

The Topeka *Daily Kansas State Journal* had this to say:

"Luke Short, over whom all this Dodge City excitement and sensation has been created, doesn't look like a man that would be dangerous to let live in any community. In fact he is a regular dandy, quite handsome, and Dr. Galland says, a perfect ladies' man. He dresses fashionably, is particular to his appearance, and always takes pains to look as neat as possible. At Dodge City he associates with the very best elements, and leads in almost every social event that is gotten up. Dr. Galland thinks the ladies will yet be heard from in Mr. Short's behalf. They have been very anxious to get up a petition among themselves to send to the Governor and it will probably come yet."

And then there was this, in part, from the Kansas City, Missouri, *Journal:*

"Yesterday a new man arrived on the scene who is destined to play a part in a great tragedy. This man is Bat Masterson, ex-sheriff of Ford County, and one of the most dangerous men the West has ever produced. A few years ago he incurred the enmity of the same men that drove Short away, and he was exiled on pain of death if he returned. His presence in Kansas City means just one thing, and that he is going to visit Dodge City. Masterson precedes by twenty-four hours a few pleasant gentlemen who are all on their way to a tea party at Dodge. One of them is Wyatt Earp, the famous marshal of Dodge, another is Joe Lowe, otherwise known as Rowdy Joe; and still another is Shotgun Collin; but worse than all is another ex-citizen and officer of Dodge, the famous Doc Holliday."

The paper went on to state that Luke Short had killed several men himself, and was utterly devoid of fear.

Things were heating up and the telegrams literally flew. Sheriff Hinkle, in Dodge, heard that Luke had the famous gunfighters coming on his behalf, and frantically wired the Governor for assistance. The Governor was getting nervous himself, and sent Colonel Thomas Moonlight to see if he could bring peace between the factions before the gun battle began.

In Dodge, Moonlight finally got an agreement from the Reformers that Short could come back to Dodge for ten days in order to settle his affairs. This was completely unacceptable to Luke. He felt that he had been wronged, and he wasn't going to give Webster, Deger, and his crowd the satisfaction of running him out of town.

Next, Robert Wright, George Hoover, and Chalk Beeson came to Topeka and held a meeting with Luke and Bat Masterson. They listened to Luke's complaints but nothing was settled. He absolutely refused any compromise on his part, saying he'd been treated badly by Webster, Deger, and Nixon, and the only thing that would satisfy him was to have all charges dropped, and that he be permitted to return to Dodge, and continue to manage the Long Branch as he had in the past.

The three men returned to Dodge and to a worried mayor and city council.

On May 31, 1883, Luke's emissaries, Wyatt Earp, Doc Holliday, and several other noted gunmen, arrived in Dodge. They immediately were met at the train station by Prairie Dog Dave Morrow, who was a city policeman. Wyatt asked Dave about the trouble, and Dave admitted that Luke Short had not been treated fairly, and had been railroaded out of town. Dave told Wyatt that many of the leading townspeople felt the same way, but were afraid to buck Webster, Deger, and Hinkle. While Wyatt had Dave at a disadvantage, he bulldozed Dave into deputizing himself and all his friends so they wouldn't have to take off their six-shooters. As soon as Sheriff Hinkle heard this, he frantically petitioned the Governor for troops. Other gunfighters, who were friendly to Luke, quietly drifted into town, and Hinkle's fears increased. Luke, Bat Masterson, and Billy Petillon waited quietly in Kinsley, thirty-two miles east of Dodge. Wyatt Earp showed up on the train the next day and told them that he had talked to the opposition, and they were ready to compromise. Luke and his friends returned triumphantly to Dodge.

There was no doubt that Luke, with the backing of his many friends had won, but Webster, Deger and the rest had to save face, so an agreement was reached whereby all charges against Luke were dropped, and he would be able to remain in Dodge to pursue his business at the Long Branch. Gambling could go on, however there would have to be a screen between the gambling areas and the saloons or dance halls. Women were to be allowed in the saloons and dance halls, but would be more closely supervised. Luke and his supporters agreed to the terms.

By the time Colonel Moonlight arrived, the Saloon War was settling down to a peaceful conclusion. Moonlight ordered a state militia to be organized in Dodge to keep the peace; the unit was called the Glick Guards and was comprised of both pro-Short and pro-Deger men. Luke's friend, Pat Sughrue, was appointed captain.

Many of the townspeople made a point of stopping Luke on the street and telling him they thought he had been treated badly; and, of course, many of them had been afraid to openly side with him against the opposition.

There were a lot of former Dodge City residents still visiting in the town, many of them were oldtimers who remembered Dodge when it was a tough town—but not so petty. The group all gathered at the Long Branch Saloon, and the drinks were on the house, as they reminisced about simpler times. Some of them suggested they have a photograph taken to mark the celebration of their getting together again, and their victory in the saloon war. They

185

posed for the now famous photograph which they self-captioned, perhaps with a smile, *The Dodge City Peace Commission.*

We see them standing stiffly there, in their old-time suits, serious, with not a trace of a smile. In the back row are William Harris, Luke Short, Bat Masterson, and W.F Petillon. Seated in front, are, Charlie Bassett, Wyatt Earp, Frank McLain, and Neil Brown.

Shortly after the photograph was taken, Wyatt Earp, Doc Holliday, and "Shotgun" Collins went back to Colorado.[1]

It was hard for Luke to forget the way some of the people had turned away from him when it looked like Webster and Deger had the winning side.

In September, Bat Masterson was back from Colorado. Luke told Bill Harris and Bat how he felt about the future of gambling and the saloon business in Kansas. Instinct told him the gambling business in Kansas was about over.

Bill Harris pursed his lips thoughtfully. "If you think that, Luke, maybe we ought to sell the place while we can get something for it."

"Who to?"

"I know someone who is interested right now," Harris said.

A few days later, Harris and Short sold the business to Roy Drake and Frank Warren. Warren was the son of Loren Warren, the freighter killed and scalped by Indians back in 1874.

When the transaction was completed, Bat Masterson looked at Luke and said, "I think we need a change of scenery, pardner. Which way you want to go?"

Luke was thoughtful for a moment, then spoke in his soft Texas voice, "Let's go down to Fort Worth, and see if there's any action there. Besides, I'd like to see my family; I haven't seen them since I was a scared kid of thirteen."

CHAPTER TWENTY

Fort Worth had been named for General W. J. Worth, a New Yorker, who was in charge of the army post near the Trinity River in 1849. After the Civil War, Fort Worth had been the gathering place for longhorn herds which came from all over Texas, some as far away as San Angelo, San Antonio, and the Gulf. The trail herds formed up on the banks of the wandering Trinity, then headed north in herds of 2,000 or 2,500 to the railroads of Kansas.

Over the years the town formed around Main Street, which ran from the courthouse down to the stockyards. By 1876, the year Dodge City became the premier longhorn railhead, there were more than 8,000 people in Fort Worth.

Fort Worth, like any other boomtown, was not short on saloons or gambling halls—or prostitutes—to entertain the *vaqueros*, freighters, cowboys and soldiers who made up the citizenry. A street car drawn by mules graced the main street, adding to the cosmopolitan outlook.

In 1883, when Luke and Bat Masterson rolled into town, Fort Worth had grown to a city of more than 20,000 souls. Main Street was lined with hotels, restaurants, and various other enterprising businesses. The two friends took rooms at the Mansion Hotel, next to the post office and settled in.

After the stress of the past months in Dodge, Luke unwound and began to look around him. He and Bat rented horses and rode out into the country. The land was thick with trees, but much of it was being cleared. The soil was rich and black, and Luke knew it would all soon be in crops. The Texas and Pacific Railroad ran east and west, and the Gulf, Colorado and Santa Fe soon expected to connect with the Atchinson, Topeka and Santa Fe up north in Kansas. As soon as the railroads were connected, Dodge would lose its longhorn business. This could not be plainer to Luke.

One night while Luke and Bat were having dinner in the opulent White Elephant Saloon and Restaurant, Luke said to his friend, "I really like this town, Bat." A strange look touched his face. "You know, I've spent a lot of years on the move going from one boomtown to another. I think I'm ready to settle down for good. It seems mighty peaceful here. Wouldn't it be nice to run an honest gambling house—and not have to pack a six-shooter?"

Bat laughed. "You have gambling, you'll always have some sorehead that will challenge you."

The *Democrat*, a Fort Worth daily, had followed the "Dodge City War," as had the entire nation, and Bat and Luke, once recognized by the citizenry, were the center of attention. As with all men who'd won out in gunfights, their exploits had been exaggerated throughout the years until Bat was reported to have killed twenty-six men. Luke, only slightly less. All this must have brought smiles to the two men's faces. They were treated as royalty, and often referred to as *Colonel.*

Luke and Bat met Jake Johnson, the owner of the White Elephant. Luke took to the friendly man immediately. Jake wasn't into the gambling business himself, but he leased space upstairs to a man who banked a few games. One night Luke and Bat decided to buck the tiger. Luke was lucky that night, and asked the bank to raise the limit. In an attempt to recoup his losses, the banker agreed, and by daylight Luke had broken his bank.

As Luke was having breakfast in the restaurant below, Jake Johnson stopped by to congratulate him. He told Luke that the gambler was desperately trying to raise enough money to open another bank.

Jake was silent for a long moment, watching Luke eat his steak and eggs. "I've heard a lot about you. They say you're an honest gambler—and that your word is good. Would you be interested in part of the action here?"

Luke thought it over. "Tell me what you have in mind," he replied.

"I'm only interested in managing the saloon and restaurant." Jake said. "I've kinda been looking for someone of your stature—and someone with the money—to set up and manage a first class gambling establishment upstairs. Are you interested?"

Luke had come to Fort Worth with that idea and here now, was a man offering him the opportunity. Luke liked the town of Fort Worth immensely and thought it had a great future. He could think of no better place to invest his money. He was also a good judge of men. He instinctively knew he and Jake Johnson would compliment one another, and together they could make the White Elephant Fort Worth's premier saloon, restaurant, and gambling establishment.

"Let's go up and look at the upper floor," Luke said when he had finished his breakfast.

Upstairs the gambler, who had lost to Luke, was packing up his faro layout and his dealers were carrying their equipment down to the street. Luke studied the large hall and considered its possibilities.

"I'd want to refurbish it completely," Luke said to Jake, "chandeliers, carpeting, wall paintings, mahogany furniture, and layouts. We could put up a partition over there in the corner and have a lounge where gentlemen could sit in comfortable chairs and read or drink between their time at the tables."

"That sounds fine to me, Luke," Jake said.

They went downstairs and had a brandy at the bar.

"I have to go back to Dodge and settle up my business," Luke said. "Then I'll come back here and we'll get going. Tell me, Jake, how do you want to do this? Do you want me to lease the upstairs, or are you interested in a partnership in the whole business?"

It developed that Jake Johnson had spent most of his capitol in renovating the restaurant and saloon and he needed a partner with money. Luke liked what Jake had done, and the clientele of the establishment. Then and there the partnership was born. Jake ordered another brandy for them, and they shook hands to bind their agreement.

Luke had one thing to do before going back to Dodge. He left Masterson to his gambling, rented a team and buckboard and began shopping for the family he'd not seen for 15 years. He stopped in a variety of shops along Main Street and filled trunks with bolts of dress materials and lace trim and other fine gifts for his mother and sisters; for his father and two brothers still living at home, he bought new saddles and boots. With the trunks and other gear lashed to the bed behind the buckboard seat, he set out early one morning, heading north toward the Red River.

He took a rifle with him, but it was more a habit rather than a necessity. The Comanches and Kiowas were gone to the reservations. Out in New Mexico and Arizona a few bands of renegade Apaches were on the loose, but for the most part, the county was safe for travel.

Much of the way, Luke followed the old cattle trail toward Red River Crossing. He stayed overnight at a roadhouse, and was off at first light, still headed north. At Saint Jo, he turned east into Cooke County. He knew the family had moved into

Grayson County, after he had left home, for throughout the years, letters from his mother had somehow found him in Deadwood, Sidney, Cheyenne, Denver, Leadville, Tombstone or Dodge. He wondered how they would all look. His father would now be seventy-one years of age, his mother, Hettie, fifty-six. Even the youngest of his siblings, Will, would be almost sixteen. From his mother's last letter, Luke knew his four other brothers, John, Joe, Young and Henry, were out in west Texas gathering cattle to start a ranch somewhere near San Angelo.

At Whitesboro he got directions to the Short's farm, and traveled on east. The country was getting settled and he could go into a farm yard every now and then and be invited to water his horse at the trough and have a cold drink, himself, from the well. These were people who no longer feared raiding Indians. People making the most of the rich soil with crops of wheat and corn, cotton, and sorghum.

When he came to a fork in the road with a weathered board that read *Short*, he turned and followed the winding wagon road.

As he came up the road to the clapboard house, he saw a slip of a woman hanging out clothes on a clothesline in the yard. The woman in her long dress was standing there, shading her eyes with her hand, watching him come up the lane. Luke felt a pang of emotion then, remembering the nights she'd stayed up with him when he'd been a sickly boy. He also remembered the nights when Pappy, John, Joe and Young were away and he and his mother had protected the little ones and old Grandpap from Comanches and Kiowas.

Luke pulled the horses up and set the friction brake. He tied the reins to the brake handle and stepped down, suddenly realizing she hadn't recognized him.

"Is this the place of Josiah Washington and Hettie Short?" he asked.

The wiry little woman studied the elegant stranger with the handlebar moustache. He was wearing a pearl grey suit with a matching flat brimmed Stetson. "Mr. Short is out in the fields somewhere," his mother said.

Luke watched his mother, then began to grin. "Mama," he said, "don't you know your own son?"

She stood there in shock, then realization flooded her lined face. "Luke!" She said. "You've come home!"

She came running to him then and hugged and kissed him, then ran toward the house calling, "Belle, Luke has come home!"

There was quite a reunion that night when his father and brothers, George and Will, came in from the fields. Will was sent to tell his sister, Mary, that Luke was back and soon she came with her husband in a buckboard from their home which was not far away.

After supper Luke gave out the presents he'd brought for his parents and brothers and sisters.

When one of his sisters asked him why he hadn't come home to see them before, Luke grinned, and said, "Well, I guess I was afraid Pappy would take his razor strap to me." He paused then, and turned serious. "Also, I made up my mind long time ago that I wouldn't come back until I was successful."

The family kept asking questions, and soon Luke found himself telling them of his cattle drives, the rich mining towns of Colorado, and of Tombstone, of Ogallala, Sidney, Deadwood, and Cheyenne. He spoke of riding dispatch and scouting with General Crook and Major Thornburgh, and of his recent problems in Dodge City, and now, of his buying into the White Elephant in Fort Worth.

When everyone else had gone to bed, Luke and his mother sat at the table with a cup of coffee, talking. His mother at last spoke of the terror she'd lived through when all the grown men of the family had been gone, and she and Luke had had to fight off the Indians.

She recalled the time when Comanches had prowled in the dark around the house and taken all their horses. The Indians felt so secure, that they had camped nearby for the night. Luke was just twelve, but he had slipped out of the house and ran for miles for help. He had gathered their settler friends and the rescue party had returned and killed many of the Comanches. They had routed the rest, and recovered all of their horses.

"How did all of us live through those dreadful years, Luke?" She asked in wonder.

"Because we're tough, Mama."

Later his mother asked, "Are all those things they say about you in the papers true?"

"About me being a gunfighter and killing twenty-some men? No, it's not true. I have killed some men, Mama, but in every case I didn't start it. I don't go looking for trouble."

Luke had noticed that his youngest brother, Will, acted a little peculiar. When he mentioned it, Hettie told him Will had been thrown from a bucking horse, and had landed on his head. She said that he hadn't been quite the same since the accident.

Hettie said his other brothers wanted the rest of the family to move out to San Angelo as soon as they got settled, probably sometime in the spring. Hettie said Wash was getting to the point where the farm work was hard for him, and they already had a buyer for their farm.

Luke stayed with his family for several days. Just before he left, he gave his mother some money and told her to let him know if she ever needed anything. There is no doubt that he had tender feelings for this small, steadfast woman who had given him birth and cared for him when he had been a sickly boy.

He left the following morning, telling his family he would be in business in Fort Worth now and hoped they would come visit him and his wife.

CHAPTER TWENTY-ONE

When Luke came back to Fort Worth, he found Bat Masterson riding high from a run of luck at the gaming tables in town. Luke knew he still had to go back to Dodge one more time to sign the final papers for the Long Branch sale. There was one more thing: in Topeka, he had talked to a lawyer about suing Dodge City for all the money he'd lost while the Long Branch had been closed when he'd been run out of town by Mayor Deger and Sheriff Hinkle. The lawyer had told Luke they could win such a case, and was ready to go ahead with it. Luke told Bat about this, and Bat was all for it, and said he was ready to leave Fort Worth, too. They left the next day.

In Topeka, Kansas, Luke sighed the papers suing the City of Dodge, and Mayor Deger and City Marshal Hinkle, in particular of unlawfully forcing him to leave town, and for monies lost while his place of business was closed up. His suit was for $15,000.[1]

Luke and Bat went on to Dodge, where Luke met with Bill Harris and the two men who were buying the Long Branch business, and the sale was finalized.

After a few days Bat went on to Trinidad, Colorado, and soon was embroiled in controversy with Marshal Lou Kreeger, of that city.

Luke told his old friend, Bill Harris, of his intentions to go into business with Jake Johnson in Fort Worth, and Harris said he thought it was a good move for Luke, for he was sure that Dodge City would be through as a trail town within two years. In this he was correct: the town would flourish as a farming center in the years to come, but the high rolling saloon keepers and gamblers would soon have to find new country. In fact, in 1885 the temperance movement was at its height in Kansas, and selling liquor was banned in Dodge. The saloon signs were taken down, and the saloon owners put up "Drug Store" signs, and sold liquor "for medicinal purposes only." Even the renowned Long Branch Saloon, which had been the premier watering hole during the heyday of the big Texas cattle drives was christened, the "Long Branch Temperance Hall." Some of the saloons were called art galleries, as they tried to get by the new ordinance. It was a sad day for the old buffalo hunters and for the remainder of the Gang which had been for an open town for the cowboys. It was truly the end of the era, and Luke was glad to be leaving it.

Luke and his friend Charlie Bassett soon left for a trip back east, where they visited friends in Kansas City and gambled. They went on to New York City, and Luke introduced Bassett to his beautiful Hettie.

Luke also took advantage of this trip to order materials and fixtures for the sumptuous gambling hall he planned for the upstairs of the White Elephant in Fort Worth.

In early 1884 Luke was back in Fort Worth with Hettie. He rented an apartment at the Lindell Hotel near the White Elephant, and he and Hettie settled in.

He and Jake Johnson had drawn up the papers of partnership, and they were finalized. The materials and fixtures Luke had ordered from the East soon arrived and the renovation of the upstairs gambling rooms began under a contractor Luke had hired.

By spring the work was finished and there was a Grand Opening. Bat Masterson, who periodically hit all the gambling towns of the west, said this about Luke's place: "The White Elephant in Fort Worth is one of the largest and most costliest establishments of its kind in the entire southwest."

It was opulent. Crystal chandeliers hung from the high ceiling, illuminating oil paintings of classical scenes. The poker and *vingt-et-un* tables were built of mahogany and covered with green cloth. The faro layouts were works of art, the suit of spades cards were inlaid in a rosewood frame, and the case-keeper showed the cards played with ivory counters. There was a roulette wheel, and even a keno table, which was becoming popular in upper social circles, and also among the younger people of the town. This might seem strange to the old-time gamblers, but it didn't faze Luke. If that's what the gamblers wanted, that's what he'd give them. The gaming room had rich drapes and thick carpets, and waiters wearing tails served drinks from the bar.

The square footage of the upper floor of the White Elephant was enormous and when Luke had first drawn up the plans, he found there was enough room left to build an apartment for himself and Hettie.

After the grand opening of the gambling hall, Luke put the crew of carpenters to work on a two bedroom apartment. To isolate the apartment from the sound of the gambling rooms, the carpenters built a sixteen inch double wall and filled it with sawdust. Windows were installed on the back side, and an outside stairway gave access to these private rooms. Luke also had a dumbwaiter installed so he could have their food sent up from the restaurant below. When everything was finished and the apartment furnished, Luke and Hettie moved their things from the Lindell Hotel on Bluff Street, and settled in.

There was precious little that he owned except for two large trunks. One held his custom-made wardrobe, and the other was filled with his books. The money which had made all this possible came from ten years of working mining and cattle towns, and his stints in Nebraska trading with the Indians.

The life of a gambler was an inverted life; the night was spent working, the day sleeping. Typically, Luke arose, bathed, and dressed around eleven o'clock in the morning. He would descend to the White Elephant Restaurant and have a leisurely breakfast, perhaps talk to his partner, Jake Johnson, then walk down Main Street, an elegant man, faultlessly dressed, with a gold-headed cane beneath his arm. He was soft-spoken, a self-educated man who could talk on any subject under the sun, quote poetry, or delve into the theories of Darwin.

Though he came from a religious family, Luke, by the time of his coming to Fort Worth, was a confirmed agnostic. Not that he had anything against the churches; in fact, he always had given generously to them. He believed most people needed religion. For himself, he was neither a believer, nor disbeliever. He didn't worry himself about death. When it came, he would accept it, just as he accepted the life he had lived, the good along with the bad.

Luke soon knew all the business people along Main Street and during his walks would stop in and visit. Sometimes he would rent horses at the nearest livery, and he and Hettie would ride out into the country, Hettie with her long skirt draped over a side-saddle. On a Sunday, Luke and Hettie could often be seen in a light buggy with a canvas top, with Luke driving a matched team of horses.

The combination of Luke Short and Jake Johnson made the White Elephant a gold mine. Its opulent restaurant catered to all the high society of Fort Worth as well as to the business and professional people. The restaurant's menu was similar to what you might find at Delmonico's in New York. Indeed, Jake bragged that New York had nothing his chefs couldn't provide. Fresh oysters came from the east coast, salmon, halibut, sole and dungeness crab from the West Coast. Luke had told Jake about the glacier ice the Clarendon and Vendome Hotels had ordered from the West Coast, and Jake was the talk of the town when he had two-thousand-year-old ice shipped in from a glacier in southeastern Alaska for his New Year's party. The bar served every kind of spirits, beer, imported wine, and mixed drinks.

The White Elephant's gaming room was popular with locals and high rolling professional gamblers alike. Gamblers from all over the country stopped by to buck the tiger, and at these times Luke often took over one of the faro tables himself. Fortunes were lost and won on Luke's tables, but the house percentage was always working for him, and though he sometimes lost huge amounts when the gamblers were on a roll, he had enough of a bank to keep going and soon made it back, and more with it.

High rollers like Dick Clark, Rusty Coe, Masterson, Earp and Holliday occasionally came to gamble and socialize. John Chisum, the cattleman, came regularly until his death in late 1884. Many of the top business men in the Southwest stopped by the White Elephant to pit their money and gambling skills against Luke's. Even the Silver King himself, Horace Tabor, might roll into town in his private railroad car to buck Luke's tiger.

It was a grand time for Luke. He had the respect and friendship of the townspeople and he and Jake Johnson prospered. As the money rolled in, Luke branched out and owned, or had an interest in, several other gambling parlors. He insisted on honest games, and began to hate the sleazy gambling joints down by the stockyards. He had seen what happened to a town when tinhorn cheats moved in with their rigged games. The reformers began to put pressure on all games of chance, even the honest ones.

Although it had been years since he had actually done any physical labor, he kept up his relationship with horses. He never forgot the fine horses he'd owned over the years. Now he bought several thoroughbreds and kept them out of town on a friend's ranch where they had plenty of room, and he spent many of his afternoons exercising and training them.

Luke, much like Bat Masterson, became an authority on all kinds of sporting events, and could be expected to bet on them. He became interested in professional horse racing, and shortly thereafter, went into partnership with Jim Brown of Brenham, Texas in a racetrack. A top winning race horse of that time was named "Longfellow." One of Longfellow's sons had a fine record himself, after his owner named him "Luke Short."

In Fort Worth in 1884, Luke had his thirtieth birthday. Today it might seem unusually young for a highly successful man to have accomplished all the things he had, but this was a different era. The famous Bat Masterson was at this time thirty-one, and Wyatt Earp, thirty-six.

Luke had money rolling in from several quarters. He would bet on anything, or promote any event which caught his attention. On one occasion he offered $20,000 to John L. Sullivan and Peter Jackson to fight in Fort Worth. This was a goodly sum for a prize fight in the middle 1880's. There is no evidence of the fight being held in Fort Worth, but it shows Luke's interest. An old time Texas historian wrote that: "There was nothing 'short' about Luke Short's game. He would never turn down any size of a bet, no matter how big." Luke Short was the King of Gamblers in Fort Worth.[2]

Little is known about the women in Luke's life before he met Hettie, for he was an intensely private man, and never spoke of them. We know from various reports, however, that he had been considered a real ladies' man. After his marriage to Hettie, Luke became a devoted husband.

Hettie Short was a slim, well-built woman just a bit over five feet in height. She had blond hair and was an extremely beautiful woman. We know this from Willie Brumley, who was Luke's young cousin, the daughter of Luke Brumley, his namesake. When she was in her teens she often visited with Luke and his wife in their apartment above the White Elephant, and later in the big brick house Luke bought on a nearby street. Willie told the family that Hettie and Uncle Luke treated her "so fine." "Luke spoilt me," she later reported, "and bought me many pretty dresses and shoes—even a Japanese parasol!" Willie stated that Hettie was a gracious hostess, and they entertained a lot. Their apartment had one whole wall of books, and Luke read extensively.

Cousin Willie Brumley remembered Luke going down to the White Elephant's bar and restaurant and bringing back delicious sandwiches and pitchers of cold imported beer. She was evidently there at one of the White Elephant's New Year's parties when the chef sculpted an immense white elephant from Alaskan glacier ice. It stood in a large tin tray on a table in the dining room. The age-old ice lasting for two days before completely melting.[3]

By 1884 it looked to Luke as if this good life could go on forever, but if a fortuneteller had looked into her crystal ball to foretell his future, she would have seen a tall, good-looking man who wore two pistols at his belt. His name was Timothy Isaiah Courtright, but he was called Jim. He'd often worn his hair long, frontier style, and was referred to as "Longhaired" Jim Courtright.

Courtright had been born in Illinois in 1845, and was nine years Luke's senior. During the Civil War he'd served the

Union Army as scout under General Logan. Later he married a girl from Arkansas, left her, and drifted to Texas and tried to farm near the Trinity River on the outskirts of Fort Worth.

The farming hadn't worked out and for a time Courtright was the marshal of a town named Marshall. Later he was a law officer in Fort Worth. He was fired from this position for some discrepancies, then drifted and began drinking heavily after this, finally ending up at Mesilla, New Mexico where he was hired as a law officer. Not long afterward, he was fired, but found a position with the help of his old Civil War friend, General Logan. Ostensibly he was ranch foreman, but he and a man named Jim McIntyre were supposed to keep the ranch free of homesteaders and squatters. The two Jims got caught up in their work and ended up killing two peaceful Frenchmen in the American Valley of New Mexico.

Supporters of the squatters called it downright murder, and very likely it was. These most certainly were not honorable duels, nor anything honorable about the killings. The murders were the beginnings of Courtright's downfall, indeed, the beginning of his bitterness. Another man might have risen above it, but Jim wasn't capable of it. He returned to Fort Worth where he had a lot of friends, and hid out.

A warrant for Courtright's arrest was sworn out and New Mexico sent deputies who came to Fort Worth and arrested him. Popular feeling was that Courtright was being railroaded, and his friends planned his rescue. A Mrs. Brown, friendly toward Jim Courtright, found out where the New Mexican deputies would bring Jim for supper. She screwed a cuphook into the bottom of the table and hung two pistols there on strings. Courtright alerted to the plan, reached under the table and soon had two .45's stuck into the deputies' faces.

Courtright's friends disarmed the deputies, and he ran out the back door where a fast horse was tied, and rode away. It was similar to Butch Cassidy and Sundance's ride which occurred later in 1901. Indeed, Courtright may have shown them the way, for he hid out in South America, too.

Courtright stayed out of the country until 1886, when he apparently felt that enough witnesses had vanished or died. He returned, stood trial and was acquitted, then returned to Fort Worth and was reunited with his wife and three daughters.

Although Courtright had many friends in Fort Worth, there was no chance of him finding a place as a law officer. Here was a bitter man, who blamed everyone but himself for his predicament. He felt it was beneath his dignity to work at manual labor, and friends often made him loans which he could not pay back. He gambled and drank much of this money away.

Finally Courtright met up with another misfit named Charley Bull. Over drinks they decided to open a detective agency. They called it T. I. C. Commercial Detective Agency. On their sign, between the T. and the C. was painted a watchful eye.

Not long afterwards, Courtright began shaking down the gambling joints near the railroad tracks and stockyards. Here was a man wearing two guns, with a dreadful reputation. The saloon and gaming joint owners evidently decided it was cheaper to pay protection than try and fight him. Encouraged by this, Jim Courtright and Bull moved uptown.

Jake Johnson, Luke's partner, had long known Courtright. Indeed, Jake had known Courtright from the time he'd been marshal of Fort Worth. He not only knew him, but considered him a friend. Jake had even loaned him money after he'd returned to Fort Worth following his acquittal for murder.

Luke had ears all over town, and he quickly saw it would simply be a matter of time before Courtright put the "protection bite" on them. He mentioned it to Jake, but Jake wouldn't talk about it.

One day Courtright found Luke alone at a table upstairs drinking a cup of coffee. He sat down across from Luke and made his pitch.

Luke heard him out, sipped his coffee, then said, "I don't need protection, Jim. I handle that part of it myself. Don't have any trouble . . . and don't expect to."

Courtright's face turned red. "I guess you think you're pretty tough, huh? Killed a few Indians . . . and an ol' grey haired man in Tombstone!"

Luke studied Courtright with his steady grey eyes. He shifted his position in the chair so his open vest fell away from his right hip. The movement wasn't lost on Courtright.

"Well," Luke said, "I was *facing* Charlie Storms when I shot him. How about those two Frenchmen you murdered out in New Mexico Territory?"

Courtright's face darkened even further. He stood up abruptly. Luke rose also. "Courtright," he said, "you might bluff those tinhorns down by the stockyard—but it won't work here! You're welcome to come in here and drink and gamble, if you behave yourself, but you try any more of this protection bullshit, and I'll have the bouncer throw you out into the street."

Courtight's face turned white, and for a moment Luke thought he would draw, but the sight of the smaller man with the steady grey eyes changed his mind. He wheeled abruptly and went across the room toward the stairway.

Luke saw Jake Johnson standing on the landing watching. Courtright went past Jake without a word, and down the stairs. Jake was holding a bottle of whiskey in his hand and three glasses. He stood there a brief moment, then came across to Luke's table. He put out two glasses and poured whiskey, then sat down. Neither man said a word as they drank.

"You know, Luke," Jake said at last. "We're doing real good here. So what if we pay Jim a little . . . call it overhead."

"No! I won't be shook down."

"He's a dangerous man!"

"So am I," Luke said, and poured another drink.

"He's got a lot of pride—he won't forget this."

"I suppose not."

"Well," Jake said with a sigh, "let me talk to Jim. Maybe I can smooth it over. . . . "

"If you want, Jake, but he'll be back. I know his kind; he's a deadbeat that doesn't want to work for a living. I'm not going to help support him."

Jake Johnson found Courtright in a saloon down the street that evening, drinking and mean.

"Jim," Jake said, trying to make peace, "Luke is a generous man, but he won't be coerced!"

"We'll see about that!" Courtright said vehemently. "That son of a bitch as much accused me of *murdering* those Frenchmen in New Mexico!"

Jake saw there wasn't any use of talking any further. Things had already gone too far between the two men. Courtright couldn't back down now without losing face; he'd been steadily going downhill and the only way was up. On the other hand, Jake was beginning to realize his partner had something in him his antagonist failed to see: beneath his soft voice and elegant clothes was a core of steel. He thought things out in advance, and there was no fear in the man.

Right now, Jake knew, while Courtright was getting drunk and bad-mouthing Luke to anyone who would listen, Luke was making his plan for the battle to come.

Winter came as always in that year of 1886. The Fort Worth businesses reported good times and hoped the New Year would be as good. Courtright and Bull continued to collect payoffs from the saloons and gambling halls down around the stockyards, but Luke's refusal to pay had stiffened the backs of the business owners uptown. They also refused to pay, and took a wait-and-see attitude, waiting for the fight they knew was going to be resolved.

Courtright sent Bull to Luke with an ultimatum. Luke turned his back on the messenger and told the bouncer, "Throw that deadbeat out!"

When the disheveled Bull stumbled back to the saloon where Courtright was waiting, he was wiping a bloody nose. Courtright went wild, cursing Luke and threatening what he was going to do to him. No man on earth could treat him this way, he bellowed to all who would listen. He was given to bragging when he drank, and reminded his followers of his reputation with a pistol. He bragged he'd killed ten men in duels, and that he could shoot Short down left-handed. Indeed, those that knew him also knew he *was* ambidextrous, a fine shot with either hand.

As Longhaired Jim drank and talked, the word was out that Courtright was going to get Luke Short. The gamblers downtown began to lay odds against Luke's chances. The betting moved uptown and Luke, on top of the betting percentages, could not resist those kind of odds himself.

When his partner, Jake, learned Luke had taken 3-to-1 odds, and bet $10,000 on himself, he was appalled. "How can you make a bet like that?" He demanded of Luke.

"Well," Luke said, "I just couldn't pass up the odds, Jake. If I'm just a little faster than your gunslinging friend, I'll win thirty thousand dollars."

"And if you lose—you'll be dead!"

Luke smiled and patted his partner on the shoulder. "Then I won't miss the ten thousand I put up, will I, Jake?"[4]

Christmas came and times were good at the White Elephant. On New Year's Eve, Jake had a big party with another masterpiece of carved ice from the talented chef.

Afterwards, the tables were cleared and there was a ball with Fort Worth's upper society well represented, the men in tuxedos, and their women in the latest fashionable gowns. An orchestra played the newest tunes from New York, and the old, well-loved European waltzes. Later that evening, Luke did a remarkable thing: he opened the gambling hall above to the ladies and let them play keno.

At dawn, as the exuberant guests left the White Elephant, they all agreed it had been a delightful event. All, that is, except for a brooding Jim Courtright, who had spent the night tossing down whiskies at one of the saloons down the street. He was in a mean mood, and lost no chance to bad mouth Luke Short.

Several days went by, and Courtright continued to drink heavily and make threats against Luke in the saloons. In John Stewart's saloon, he was heard to say: "God made one man superior to the other in muscular power, but when Colt made his pistol it made all men equal." Courtright then directed his remarks to a man named McCarty, saying he'd lived over his time, and no man on earth had percentage over him. He said this business would be settled shortly—that he hadn't been treated with any respect upstairs over the White Elephant.

This was drunk talk, somewhat confused, but it got back to Luke that evening. Surely Luke must have known the showdown was at hand. He had studied Courtright, and knew the man had been drinking hard and making bragging comments. He also could see Courtright had gone too far to back down now. He would have to follow through, or lose face—and that Courtright would never do.

Accordingly Luke began to reassess his own position. *If* he was killed, it would leave Hettie in partnership with Jake Johnson. Luke didn't like this option. If he died, he wanted Hettie to have plenty of money and be free of the partnership. So, on the evening of February 7, 1887, Luke called his partner into the White Elephant's office and asked him to buy out his interest. Jake was stunned at first, but Luke explained the problems if Courtright killed him. "If it'll make you feel better, Luke, okay," Jake Johnson finally said. "After it's over—I can just sign it back to you."

"We'll see about that when the time comes, but for now I want this to be completely legal. You figure out what my interest is worth to you and give me a check, and I'll sign my interest over to you."

Jake agreed, and the two men called an attorney and had papers made out and notarized that night. It might be speculated why Luke would sell out his interest in this most profitable and fashionable operation in Fort Worth. There are three reasons that are evident: first in the event he was killed, the money from the sale would take care of his wife, Hettie. Second: Jake Johnson was still a good friend of Jim Courtright, and this must have bothered Luke to think his partner had tried to talk him into paying off such a loud-mouthed bully and drunk. Third: Luke was very perceptive of the way the west was changing. He had seen it happen in Dodge City, and had sold out his interest in the Long Branch just two years before gambling was outlawed, and the temperance laws were enforced. He knew it was only a matter of time before the winds of change would prevail here in Fort Worth, too. If he lived through this duel with Courtright, he could simply lease the upstairs gambling hall from Jake, and continue on as he was.

But he did not plan for a moment on being killed, even though the odds were now four to one against him on the street; he had his plan all worked out. It was a plan that had worked before. When he had gone into full-time gambling, he'd deduced there wasn't likely to be much long range shooting. Most of the quarrels that erupted for the gambler were across the table, or at short range on the street. That's when he'd had a gunsmith cut down the barrel of his Colt .45 and had the leather holster built into his hip pocket. He kept the small holster dusted inside with talcum powder, and there wasn't a day went by that he didn't spend a few minutes practicing drawing the snub-nosed .45. Another thing Luke had learned in the fight with Charlie Storm was to crowd in close to your opponent and get the first shot off. The tremendous concussion and the blast of black powder would throw off the other man's timing. Even if the first shot wasn't to a vital area, it gave time for follow up shots.

Luke had never started a fight in his life, but he detested the bullying Courtright, and was determined to put the man out of his life forever when they met, and that meeting couldn't be far off, for the pressure was on Courtright to back up his talk.

Several days before, Bat Masterson had arrived in town, as he often did on his gambling circuits, and we have Masterson's take on the coming duel.[5] Luke told Bat of Courtright's thinly veiled hints as to the terrible things that might befall a gambling hall operator if he didn't avail himself of the services of T. I. C. Commercial Detective Agency. At one point Luke said in exasperation, "Goddammit, Bat, why can't we run an honest game of chance without having to fight every egotistical clown who fancies himself a gunman!"

On February eighth, the Fort Worth *Gazette* made this announcement:

> "Messers Jake Johnson and Luke Short made a little business deal yesterday, in which the latter sold to the other gentleman the one-third interest owned by him. Mr. Short does not contemplate any change of base, but will continue to call Fort Worth home."

This bit of news just might have nudged Jim Courtright into making his play, for he might have deduced that Luke thought he would die, and was straightening out his personal affairs. Indeed, there is no doubt the majority of the citizens of Fort Worth felt that the coming duel was a terrible mismatch. Captain Jim Gillett, who had been a Texas Ranger, and knew Courtright well, said:

"Courtright was a wizard with a Colt . . . it would have been hard to know how to lay your bet had a contest of gunplay been staged between Courtright, and any of the other noted gunfighters of the day."[6]

There is no doubt that most everyone thought the quiet, gentlemanly gambler from the White Elephant was a dead man. Certainly he was not perceived to be a *noted* gunfighter. Indeed, he had never considered himself anything but a business man—an honest gambler. If there was one man in Fort Worth who thought Luke Short had a chance of coming out of the fight with Longhaired Jim, the ambidextrous six-shooting genius with two revolvers—it was Short's good friend, Bat Masterson. Bat had seen the calm, alert gambler draw and shoot the loudmouthed Charlie Storms' heart out in front of the Oriental Saloon in Tombstone six years before. And Bat was also one of the few people Luke had told of killing nine Indians and two white men in Nebraska.

In his reminiscences Bat Masterson didn't report if he took the long odds to bet on the success of his friend in Fort Worth. Perhaps he might have thought it unseemly to admit that he had. In any event, we know that a real high rolling gambler of Masterson's caliber, could have no more passed up a wager on this duel than he could have gone to a prize fight without making a bet.

Clouds had rolled in from the Gulf and Fort Worth was under a leaden sky with scattered showers. It was still February, and with the rain, there was a definite chill to the air. Luke invited Bat to have dinner with Hettie and him in the apartment. The menu was ordered by Luke from the White Elephant's restaurant, and delivered piping hot in the dumbwaiter which serviced Luke's apartment from the kitchen below.

After wine and dinner cigars, Bat and Luke went into the gaming room next door, Luke to relieve one of his faro dealers, and Bat to try his hand at poker. There was an unwritten rule between the friends to never buck the faro tiger at the other's place of business.

On the morning of February eighth, the weather was still miserable; more grey clouds from the Gulf, and more scattered showers. Luke, as usual, rose late and bathed. He shaved with his ivory handled straight razor, splashed cologne onto his face, then dressed carefully. He sat down at the table in his library and cleaned his shortened Colt .45. Hettie watched silently as Luke lightly oiled the mechanism, then loaded the cylinder, leaving an empty chamber under the hammer. He washed his hands carefully and dusted the inside of the built-in leather holster with talcum powder.

"Do you think it will be today?" Hettie asked at last.

"I think so," Luke said, pointing to the notice in the *Gazette* that lay open on the table, the notice mentioning Luke had sold his interest in the White Elephant to Jake Johnson. "This will make Courtright think he's got me on the run." Luke settled the snub-nosed Colt in the leather holster on his right hip, then put on his embroidered vest, but this time he didn't button it, nor did he put his Jürgensens gold watch into the watch pocket with its gold nugget chain and carved ivory fob. He kissed Hettie, thankful she was not an hysterical woman, put on his flat crowned Stetson and went down the outside stairway and around the alley into the saloon entrance.

Luke had coffee, then a late breakfast in the White Elephant's restaurant. His partner, Jake Johnson, found him there and they talked of everything but the one subject on both their minds—Courtright. Due to the chilly weather, business was slow in both the bar and restaurant.

After eating Luke strolled to a nearby shoeshine parlor and

had his boots cleaned and shined. A friend told him Jim Courtright was down the street in a saloon, drinking and still making threats about what he was going to do to Luke. Luke nodded, and paid for the shoeshine. He lighted a cigar and walked into the shooting gallery next to the White Elephant and talked with the manager, Ella Blackwell. In the shooting gallery were B. F. Herring and William Allison. Luke spoke to them, noticing their nervousness. When they left, Luke went back to the White Elephant and upstairs to the gambling rooms.

Few men were gambling this early, but, by six that evening, business was picking up. A little later Jake Johnson came by the billiards room where Luke and Bat Masterson were sitting by themselves talking. Jake had come in from the street and said the drizzle had stopped and the sky was clearing. Presently he went down into the saloon and left the two men alone.

A little after eight o'clock, Jake came back. He wore a worried look, then told Luke that Jim Courtright wanted to talk to him.

"I think we can work this out without trouble, Luke," Jake said. "I'll go out with you."

Luke looked at Bat Masterson a long moment, then nodded briefly, and stood up. He put his hand on his Colt, then let the tail of his loose vest settle over the butt of the pistol.

"All right, Jake," Luke said. "Let's go."

Courtright was standing in front of the shooting gallery. Luke and Jake Johnson walked to within a few feet of Courtright, Jake to the side of the sidewalk, out of the line of fire. Luke, deliberately moved closer, and this spooked Courtright. "Don't you pull a gun on me!" Courtright shouted.

This was a standard warning, for it could later be used as evidence that its author was only defending himself.

"I haven't got any gun here, Jim," Luke said, lifting the

front of his loose vest to show he was not wearing a gunbelt. At this point he thought possibly he could avoid a gunfight, but he was watching Courtright and saw his hand go for his pistol. Luke drew the short barreled Colt from his hip in one smooth motion and fired.

There was a tremendous explosion as the Colt went off, and the blue-black smoke from the black powder almost obscured Courtright. Luke didn't know if his first shot had been a good one, only that it had been the first shot fired. He moved right against Courtright and fired again, this one right into the chest. He saw Courtright trying to shift his revolver into his left hand, and fired three more shots into Courtright at pointblank range. Courtright fell sideways into Blackwell's shooting gallery.

Bony Tucker, a young policeman, was less than a block away, talking to his brother, Rowan. When he heard the shots, he and Rowan ran up the street to the shooting galley. He only saw Luke Short at first, he said later, then he saw Courtright laying half into the shooting gallery with his legs out onto the sidewalk. Luke was standing looking down at Courtright, the snub-nosed Colt in his hand by his side.

Bony, afraid Luke might shoot him in the excitement of the moment, moved behind him and grabbed his pistol.

"It's empty, Bony," Luke said quietly.

Luke's first bullet had smashed the thumb of Courtright's gun hand. Desperately, Courtright had tried the "border shift" instead of drawing his left hand Colt, but it had been a futile move, for the bullet which had mangled his thumb had damaged the cylinder of his pistol so that it couldn't properly rotate.

After Bony Tucker had taken Luke's Colt, he knelt beside Courtright. He had this to say in his deposition:

"When I reached him he was dying and though I bent over and spoke to him, he never articulated a syllable. He still grasped his gun in one hand, a .45 of the same make as the one that killed him. The chambers were still filled with cartridges, showing that he failed to get in a shot.

"The bullets had taken effect. One broke his thumb, the second passed through his heart, and the third struck him in the shoulder. I believe it was the second shot that killed him. He was a dead man within five minutes of the time I reached him. Sheriff Shipp, Marshal Rea, Rowan Tucker and myself took Short to the county jail."

The next day Jake Johnson got Attorney Steadman to represent Luke, and at the inquest the witnesses gave testimony. W. A. James went on the stand and told of the threats he'd heard Jim Courtright make the night before to a man named McCarty when speaking of Luke.

The only person who had seen and heard the entire shooting incident was Jake Johnson. This is his statement:

"I alone was present when the difficulty between Short and Courtright occurred. I saw no one else there. When Courtright was shot, he fell into the shooting gallery. Courtright got his pistol out of the scabbard before he was shot. He fell at the first fire. I did not know there was going to be any difficulty when I called Short out. Courtright and I were talking two or three minutes when I called Short out. He consented to have a talk with Luke and I called Luke out. They were three or four feet apart while talking—Luke had his thumbs in the armholes of his vest and he dropped them in front of him, and Courtright said: 'You needn't be getting out your gun.'

"Luke said, 'I haven't got any gun here, Jim' and raised up his vest to show him.

"Courtright then pulled his pistol. He (Luke) drew his and commenced to fire. One standing in the shooting gallery could not see the parties at the beginning of the difficulty.

214

"Short and I are good friends and partners. I was as good a friend to Courtright as I am to Short."[7]

Bony Tucker gave testimony, as did Policeman Fulford, then Mr. Alex Steadman arose and asked the justice for bail for his client in the amount of $2,000.

Justice Smith said after hearing the evidence, he thought that a bond of $2,000 was reasonable, and set that amount.

Jake Johnson, W. T. Maddox, Robert McCarty, and Alex Steadman became bondsmen, and Luke was released.

According to author Alfred Henry Lewis, Bat Masterson told him sometime after the turn of the century of that night Luke had spent in the Fort Worth County Jail. Apparently some of Courtright's rowdy friends began to talk of a lynching. Bat got word of the proposed lynching and went to the sheriff and talked him into allowing Bat to spend the night with Luke. Bat took a pair of six-shooters for himself and a pair for Luke, and apparently the crowd of Courtright's admirers decided they had better leave the two armed men alone.

The day following the gunfight, the Fort Worth *Gazette* interviewed Luke in the county jail. Luke told his story of the affair, leaving out any mention of Courtright's efforts to collect "protection" money from him. Perhaps Luke, ever the gentleman, hesitated to bring more shame upon the widow and daughters of the slain man. They had already suffered enough from the charges of murder against Jim in New Mexico and from his subsequent escape to South America.[8]

This was the *Gazette's* description of Luke at the interview:

"Luke Short is a small man of quiet and gentlemanly manners. There is nothing about him suggestive of the desperado. He is one of the most widely known sporting men in the West and has a reputation of being generous to a fault. No man can be more unobtrusive in demeanor, yet he is known to be thoroughly game.

"Several years ago in Arizona he fought a duel with one of the most desperate men in the territory. His first bullet pierced his opponent's heart, the second broke his neck. The duel was pushed on him by the other and public sympathy fully sustained Short."

Courtright, Civil War scout, failed farmer, former peace officer, gambler, alleged murderer, gunfighter, shakedown artist, husband, father of three lovely daughters, died without funds and in debt; the city of Fort Worth provided the money for a grand funeral. So much for the sentimentality of the times. A string of carriages six blocks long followed his casket to Oakwood Cemetery.

CHAPTER TWENTY-TWO

Perhaps a sign of the times was that after killing Courtright, Luke was taken into custody not by a town marshal, or county sheriff, but by Bony Tucker and Officer Fulford, city policemen dressed in uniforms.

A few days after Luke was released from the county jail by Justice Smith, Jake Johnson asked Luke if he would like to tear up the contract of sale and the check, and resume partnership in the White Elephant. Although Luke was appreciative of Jake's testimony which had contributed to his release on a self-defense plea, he had to have had misgivings about Jake's friendship with Courtright, a man who was not only a drunken braggart, but a mean spirited racketeer as well. In any event, Luke turned down Jake's offer to buy back into the ownership of the White Elephant. Instead, he proposed to lease the upstairs gaming rooms from Jake at a fixed rate. Since the business was making an enormous profit, Jake probably preferred this arrangement.

One of the things we notice about Luke Short, was his uncanny perception of the future. The long, hard cattle drives were no more; the trail towns were not completely gone, but had evolved and become quiet little farming communities. The temperance and antigambling movements were gaining ground all over the West, and the free and easy life of the frontiersmen and their inclinations to booze, gambling and easy women would soon be a thing of the past. The frontier towns were changing to accommodate the wives and families of the business and agricultural communities. More churches were built and the hardshelled preachers railed against the sinful lives of the very people who had made the frontier safe enough for them to be there.

Certainly Luke was perceptive enough to see the writing upon the wall, and he must have hated it, but his decision to lease the upstairs gambling hall at the White Elephant instead of buying back into the partnership was wise, for in December of 1887, open door gambling was barred in Fort Worth.

Luke had bought a large, elegant brick home on a quiet oak-lined street of Fort Worth, and he and Hettie moved in, and began living a quieter life. Luke still operated the White Elephant gaming rooms, though his payoffs to the police had now increased. He also had controlling interests in several other gambling establishments, but as the reformers toughened their rhetoric, Luke became enraged with the crooked games run by several operators down by the stockyards. One operator, Charlie Wright, with whom Luke had previously had trouble with in Chicago and Leadville, was the leader of this element. Doc Holliday had come close to killing the crooked gambler in New Mexico, and Luke was now sorry he had not. Luke knew if Wright and his kind kept up their crooked games and habits of rolling cowboys, who drove cattle to the stockyards to be shipped east by rail, the authorities would soon shut down all gambling in Fort Worth. Luke had accosted Charlie Wright on the street and warned him of the consequences if he persisted in rolling the cowboys and stockyard workers who frequented his games.

This situation continued and Luke became more enraged as time went on. He was also beginning to have health problems, and perhaps this increased his irritation with Charlie Wright. One December day in 1890, Luke heard from friends downtown that Wright had set up a young cattleman in his clip joint. He had taken the naive man for his entire stake after selling his cattle. Luke's informant said Wright and his confederates had doctored the young buyer's whiskey with a strong sleeping potion. Whether this information was correct or not, it fitted in with what he knew about Wright. In a rage, Luke stuck his Colt into his hip pocket sheath and headed downtown.

When he entered Wright's gambling room above the Bank Saloon, he pulled out his six-shooter and ran the card dealers and Wright's customers outside. Using the leg off a table, he broke up the crooked faro box layout, the roulette wheel, and anything else which could be damaged. His anger was monumental, and Wright fled before it along with the rest. Luke sent word to Wright to get out of town, then headed home.

But Charlie Wright was determined, and he soon was back in business and up to his old tricks above the Bank Saloon, fleecing cowboys, along with the men who worked the trains and at the freight yards—anyone who had the poor sense to step into his joint. After a Southern Pacific brakeman was robbed at Wright's, Luke went again alone to Wright's gambling house. He met a Negro coming down the outside stairway with a tray of dirty glasses. He asked the man what they were doing up in Wright's. Gambling, the Negro said, adding that he had just taken some of the players drinks from the saloon.

Luke told the man to put down the tray and to go back up the stairway. Luke closely followed him, then burst into the gambling hall with his six-shooter in his hand and yelled for the dealers and gamblers to clear out. They obeyed and Luke put away his pistol and picked up a chair and began breaking up the gambling equipment again.

When he was finished, he put down the chair, looked

around to see if he had missed anything, then started down the short hallway to the outside stairs. He heard a sound, and was beginning to turn, when he was hit by the blast of a shotgun. The blast hit him in his left leg and back, and tore away part of his left thumb.

Luke pulled his six-shooter and whirled and shot at the dim figure of the man who held the shotgun. There was a cry of pain and the shotgun dropped to the floor. Luke fired other shots as the figure vanished, then staggered down the stairway, while reloading his gun with his bloody left hand.

The Negro, who led him upstairs, was standing by the front door of the Bank Saloon.

"I'm hit," Luke said. "Would you please go down the street and send a hack to pick me up?"

"Sho, Mistah Luke," the man said, and took off down the street at a trot.

When the hack arrived, the Negro and the hack driver helped Luke into the seat. He directed the driver to stop by the police station, where he told one of his policemen friends of the fight. He then went on the hospital and had his wounds treated. The police also found Wright at the hospital under a doctor's care for a fractured wrist. Wright was subsequently heavily fined.

Luke lost part of his thumb and had two stiffened fingers on his left hand. He also walked with a limp thereafter. A piece in the Dallas *News* about the affair concluded with: "Wright has been regarded as a terrible man, while Short's reputation is that of a man of iron nerve."

Finally, when his lease was up with Jake Johnson, Luke moved his equipment and furnishings to a building he owned. He called the new place, the Palace Royal Gambling Hall. Luke had not been happy with Jake Johnson since the killing of Courtright. Once, Johnson had bemoaned the fact that Courtright had left a widow and three daughters. Luke said caustically, "Courtright should have thought about his wife and daughters before he decided to shake me down!"

All of Luke's old White Elephant customers followed him to his new place of business, and he did very well there, and though his payoff to the police increased, he was happy to pay.

Charlie Wright had problems with his wrist which Luke's .45 had fractured. It never healed properly and Wright was not able to deal his crooked games again. He never replaced the broken gaming equipment, and soon afterward left Fort Worth.

Luke had gotten rid of one crooked gambler, but the churches and the energetic ladies of the city, who viewed gambling, drinking and commercial sex as evils to be stamped out, were finally successful. An ordinance against gambling was enforced, and the ladies saw to it neither the police nor city officials were paid off to allow gambling to continue as it had in the past.

Luke closed down his games, and sold the building to a local businessman. He moved his gambling equipment into storage, then he and Hettie took a long vacation.

In 1884, the year Luke had moved to Fort Worth from Dodge City, his brothers, John, Joe and Henry, were running cattle out in West Texas around Alpine and the Davis mountains. Later that year, they bought land around Ben Ficklin, and persuaded their parents, Wash and Hettie, to sell their ranch in Greyson County and move to Ben Ficklin. With their parents and brothers out in West Texas, Martha and Belle, now both married, also moved near their parents.

In 1889 Luke and Hettie spent several days shopping for presents for his family now living at Ben Ficklin, which was near a little Mexican town called San Angelo. They took the train west, and Luke introduced Hettie to the rest of the Short family.

Luke's notoriety followed him wherever he went, for he was one of the best known gamblers in the West, and his gunfighting abilities were magnified beyond all reason.

His recent duel with the infamous Jim Courtright made him a celebrity, and he hated it. When a newspaper reporter once asked him what he would like to have engraved on his gravestone, he answered simply, "An honest gambler."

Luke, and Hettie had a good visit with his family. His mother was worried about Luke's health. His lower legs were swollen, and some days he had difficulty even moving around.

His mother attempted to talk Luke and his wife into moving west where she could look after him if his physical condition worsened. His doctors in Fort Worth suspected he had Bright's Disease and he was trying to follow a less rich diet, and had all but quit drinking.

Luke thanked his mother, but declined, perhaps instinctively knowing the two Hetties, mother and wife, would not get along in such a situation.

Back in Fort Worth, his health seemed to improve for awhile and he talked about possibly going to British Columbia, where there was talk of a new gold strike, and the moralists did not yet hold sway.

Soon Luke was sick and incapacitated again and his doctor referred him to a specialist in Chicago. He and Hettie traveled there to see him. The doctor prescribed a new diet, no alcohol and gave him new medications.

Back in Fort Worth, Luke began to feel much better, the swelling in his legs lessened, and he sat in his brick mansion trying to decide what to do. He didn't need money, but he was only thirty-seven, and entirely too young to be idle. Besides, he missed the excitement of the gaming tables, the click of the chips and the faro dealer's, "All bets down, gentlemen—here come the cards!"

In early 1890, Luke's father died in Ben Ficklin, Texas. Josiah Washington Short was buried there in the graveyard on a bluff above the Concho River. A month later to the day, Luke's youngest brother, Will, was killed. On a rainy night during a cattle roundup, Will, riding at full gallop, hit a barbed wire fence and was thrown and killed. Will was also buried in the family plot in Ben Ficklin.

With his improved health, Luke was filled with energy. He began to follow the mineral strikes around the west. In 1890, it was supposed by many that all the rich minerals in Colorado had been found. Stream after stream, gulch after gulch had been prospected, even the tailings were reexamined. Nothing was found.

But unknown to all, even the most persistent prospectors, there lay a bonanza yet undiscovered only twenty-odd miles west of Pike's Peak. It was so rich in gold, it would make the Clear Creek strike and the South Park strike look penny-ante. The site, some of it above timberline in the thin Colorado highlands, was to become the world's greatest gold camp, but it gave no indication of its hidden wealth, for much of it was in alpine meadows and the gulch crossed basins where summer grass and wildflowers fed cattle that inhabited the area. Indeed, the creek which ran through it was named when a calf leaped a fence and broke its leg. The cowboys called the stream Cripple Creek.

One of the homesteaders, who ran a few cows there, was Bob Womack. Bob was a happy-go-lucky cowboy known for his horsemanship. Bob and his father and brother had been around the mining camps for years, before building a cabin on Cripple Creek. For years he had hoped for a big mineral strike. He wasn't particular whether it was gold or silver. Once in 1874, he'd picked up a piece of grey rock which assayed $200 a ton in gold. He thought he had it made, and for sixteen years he looked for the mother lode without finding it.

Bob, after a few shots of whiskey would inevitably begin to talk of his big find. Finally no one paid any attention to him, and he became the butt of many jokes.

The good-humored cowboy didn't let the jokes get to him; he continued to prospect and talk about all the gold in his valley. One day Bob found a man who didn't laugh at him. His name was Dr. John Grannis, a dentist who had come to Colorada's high altitude, hoping to be cured of tuberculosis. He was living at Colorado Springs when Bob met him. Dr. John had enough faith in Bob to propose a partnership. Dr. John had some money and borrowed more to stake Bob in their prospecting adventure. They agreed to split everything Bob found fifty-fifty.

Not long afterwards, Bob found a small rock with a yellow streak in it. He broke off a chunk with his pick, staked a claim, and took the sample to Colorado Springs and had a metallurgist run an assay. The assayer, Henry Lamb, soon told Womack and Dr. John the sample assayed at $250 a ton. The Cripple Creek gold rush was on.[1]

In 1891, Luke heard the news, and enthusiastically made plans to go there and build a saloon and gambling hall. Hettie, however, was not happy with Luke's plans to head to Cripple Creek. She was not satisfied his illness was gone, and in this assumption she was correct, for Luke soon was bedridden with swollen legs and puffiness of his abdomen again. His doctor prescribed a double dose of his new medication, and he was soon back on his feet.

The relapse convinced him he might live only if he began taking better care of himself. To move to Colorado with its frigid winters and almost two-mile-high elevation, was clearly foolhardy.

Luke was agonizing over all this when salvation came. It came from a friendly but strange source, from a man who could not solve his own tragic predicament, but who got Luke back into doing what he loved most. The man was the tall, elegant gambler, Dick Clark. Clark had stayed on in Tombstone, Arizona even after the mines had began to give out.

During the years Luke had owned and operated the gambling business at the White Elephant, Dick Clark had often been a visitor and participant in the big games. Now, in 1891, Dick had come to town and run into Nat Kramer in Fort Worth. Kramer told him all the gambling halls had been closed.

"And Luke?" Clark asked.

"Him, too," Kramer said, "all closed."

"I heard he's not well," Clark said.

"No."

"You know where he lives?"

"Sure," Kramer answered, "in a big brick mansion not far from here."

The two gamblers found a one-horse hack, and climbed in. A few minutes later they were in front of the Short home.

Dick Clark had, for thirty-three of his fifty-five years, been a gambler, in fact he was one of the premiere gamblers of the entire west. He had made a fortune, but had never managed his money well. For thirty of those thirty-three years, he'd lived in hotel rooms and eaten at restaurants and boarding houses. At fifty, he'd taken a hard look at his life, and not been too happy with what he saw. His health was failing, and the strain of long poker games and hours at the faro tables had taken a toll, and it clearly showed in his face. He'd recently been diagnosed with tuberculosis, and because of the pain while putting in long hours at the gambling tables, had begun drinking heavily, something he had never done before. When the booze didn't take away the pain, he started using morphine.

At last he decided to straighten himself out. He met a vivacious young French Canadian girl of seventeen and married her. He moved out of his lonely hotel rooms and bought a home in Tombstone. He filled the house with fine furniture from San Francisco and settled down. He and his wife even adopted a little girl. For awhile Dick was able to get off the morphine, and most of the booze, but when the pain worsened, he resumed taking both, and continued gambling in Tombstone. Arizona was still a territory, and so far, the moralists hadn't found a way to stop it. Dick and his wife, Louise D'Argentcout Clark, had traveled to Fort Worth to see if the gambling houses were really closed, and to see old fraternal friends.

Luke was overjoyed to see Dick when Nat Kramer knocked on his door and asked, "Guess who's out in the hack?"

When Luke learned Dick's wife, Louise, and their adopted daughter were at an uptown hotel, he insisted they were to stay with him, and sent a hack to pick them up. Hettie, along with her Negro maid, went shopping and soon returned to start dinner, while Luke showed Clark and Kramer around the big house. Clark was clearly taken with it.

"I just bought my first house in Tombstone," Dick said. "All these years I've lived out of hotel rooms. Sad isn't it?"

Luke asked, "How is Tombstone, Dick?"

"Dying," said his friend, "dying, like me," and he covered his mouth with his handkerchief and coughed and coughed.

Nat Kramer and Luke just looked at each other.

After a few drinks and dinner, Dick was himself again, witty and full of stories of the old days on the gambling circuit, of Kansas City in its heyday; he even told some stories of his Civil War days when he was a quarter-master sergeant, and beginning to learn the business of gambling.

When dinner was over, the men repaired to the library and cigars and Clark said, "Luke, I've been thinking about you and

Nat. I've got a plan for you. You've got to get back into the gambling business again!"

"How?"

"Right here!" Dick said, and pulled Luke to his feet. "How many bedrooms do you have in this big house?"

"Seven."

"See what I mean! Now, how many do you actually need?"

"Well, one for Hettie and me, one for Cousin Willy . . . and maybe a spare in case somebody visits us."

"See what I mean!" Dick said. "You have four rooms you can use for gambling." Dick pulled him down the hallway. "Knock out this wall between two bedrooms. This could be the faro room, and this one could be for poker . . . or maybe two rooms for poker!"

Dick glanced at Luke. "I know what you're thinking, Luke, but you wouldn't be sitting out in the open like in a gambling hall. You'd be in your own home, and you can *pick* the men who come to *your* home to play a game of chance. There's dozens of high rollers who would come and play big stake poker or 'buck the tiger!' By the way, where are your mechanisms?"

"In storage," Luke said.

"Get them out! All you need is a couple of poker tables and one faro layout—and you're in business. See what I mean?" Dick Clark had a big grin on his face.

"It might work." Luke finally conceded.

"Of course it'll work. Don't have anyone here who doesn't have real money. They all know you and your reputation for being square. There won't be any sore losers. The word will get around and they'll come take their chances. The best part of it is you can put your pistol away for good, Luke. There will be strictly gentlemen gamblers in your home."

Nat Kramer, caught up with the idea, said, "Maybe ol' Haw Tabor would hook his private car onto a train and come down from Colorado."

"Of course he will!" Dick Clark said.

They all sat down and Nat asked the expansive Dick to tell of the time Dick had won all the money Tabor had on him in Leadville.

"Well," Clark said, "I had cleaned him out, and Tabor asked if he could bet a carload of silver ore sitting on a siding there in Leadville. Tabor's hand was good, but I thought mine was better, and I won the carload of ore, too! It was the closest I ever came to owning a mine!" Clark said, laughing.

In a few days Clark and his lovely wife went back home to Tombstone.

CHAPTER TWENTY-THREE

After Dick Clark left Fort Worth, Luke brought in brick masons and carpenters to enlarge the library into what would become the faro room. Two of the bedrooms had a bathroom between them, and they became the poker rooms. Luke had the masons lay in another brick wall sixteen inches from the wall separating the proposed gambling rooms from the main house. The space between these two walls was sound-proofed and a new door was installed. The rooms were arranged so the customers could enter through the front door, turn to the right and go down a hallway and be in the gaming rooms without actually coming into the living part of the house. A large walk-in closet in the gaming area held an icebox, and shelves to hold the customers' own private brands of liquor.

One dark night Luke had movers bring two of his best poker tables and the more complex faro layout into the gaming rooms and set them up. When everything was ready, Luke sent out personal printed notices to all the high rolling gamblers he knew west of Kansas City, then sat back and waited. He wasn't disappointed. Two freespending cattlemen blew into town and began telephoning and sending wires to acquaintances and friends inviting them to join the fun. When the players began to show up, Luke used Nat Kramer and another of his former employees to assist him. Both men were known to be completely honest, and were well liked. Luke paid them a small percentage to collect the house share on the poker tables, although the two men were talented enough to make good money gambling on their own. Luke banked and operated the faro layout, with another former employee to act as casekeeper. He hired his maid's husband to keep the icebox filled, make drinks from the customers' own private liquor stocks, and deliver sandwiches the maid made in the kitchen. Luke and Hettie began to use the servant's entrance through the carriage house, leaving the front door exclusively for their customers. The first session was a grand success, and when it broke up early the next morning all the players were enthusiastic.

Luke was extremely pleased, for he could see the private gambling club would work out well. The class of men coming to gamble guaranteed there would be no sore losers. Many of Luke's former customers in Dallas and Fort Worth were well-to-do business men and city officials whose wives and church ministers had forced them to enforce the no-gambling ordinances. The men were doubly happy, for they had satisfied their wives' moral fervor on one hand, and at Luke's house they had a private place to socialize with their peers and gamble and drink. With these kinds of men as satisfied customers, Luke knew they would never allow him to be harassed.

Moreover, there was little overhead, no payoffs to the police or city hall, and for the first time in his gambling career, Luke was able to take off the snub-nosed Colt, put it in a drawer and forgot about it.

There were some exciting, no limit games played in the house, games which would be talked about for years to come. There were high rollers from Kansas City, New Mexico, San Antonio and El Paso, Texas, Tucson and Tombstone, Arizona. Indeed, Luke's old friend, Dick Clark, the person who had suggested this operation, often stopped by when he knew certain gamblers would be in town. Clark had for some years owned a cattle ranch on the San Pedro near Tombstone. His manager ran the spread, but being a ranch owner entitled Clark to be a member of the Cattlemen's Association.

At any cattlemen's convention, no matter if it was held in Chicago, Kansas City, Ogallala, Cheyenne or Fort Worth, you could bet on Dick Clark being there. The reason was simple: the cattle barons were, almost to a man, heavy gamblers. The personal traits which caused them to bet heavily at cards, were the same traits that moved them to gamble heavily on land, water holes, cattle, blooded bulls, and weather.

Of this august group coming from near and far to try their skill against one another, or trying to break Luke's faro bank, there were some real characters who had bet, or would bet on anything under the sun. They were a gregarious bunch for the most part, self-made men, iconoclastic in many respects, against government rules, and barbed wire, unless it was to their advantage, nesters, sheepmen, temperance societies, and antigambling ordinances.

Major Andrew Drumm had once been in a no-limit poker game in Kansas City with a wealthy cattleman and cleaned him out of cash. The cattleman still wanted to play however, so they agreed to play for cattle. Stakes were set at a one-steer ante, two-steers to open, jacks or better. By the time the game was over, Drumm had 750 steers, several bulls, a herd of two-year-old heifers, 10 blooded horses, and a lot of land in Texas.

Luke was generous to a fault. It was seldom he ever turned anyone down for a handout or a loan. Former employees and professional gamblers down on their luck were sure of a loan from Luke. They never went away from the house in Fort Worth empty-handed. On one occasion a strange request for a loan came to Luke from an old gambling friend in Denver. It was a wire that read something like this:

Am sitting in a game at the Navarre with four natural aces stop The bet across the table is $30,000 stop Desperately need to call stop Bud

The Denver gambling hall manager sent a wire also, asking Luke if he would back Bud. Luke wired back he'd make the amount good if Bud lost the hand.

Luke waited, a smile was on his lips beneath the neat moustache which was beginning to be touched with grey. He could just picture Bud sitting at a poker table, chips piled high, the players still in the game, sipping their drinks and waiting, their cards closed and gripped tightly in their hands. Very likely there were just the two men left in the hand, Bud, and the man who had raised his bet. Luke sat there, chuckling to himself as he thought of this scene, remembering his nights on the gambling circuit.

After a little more than an hour, the doorbell rang, and Luke took the telegram from the messenger boy. The wire read:

It was a helluva pot stop But four aces beat four kings any day stop Thanks old friend stop Bud

In late 1892, Luke was back in bed in a lot of pain, with a swollen abdomen and legs. There was more grey in his moustache and hair, and his face was puffy. He didn't like to see himself in the mirror. Hettie made him as comfortable as she could, but nothing seemed to help. Late in the year they took the train to Chicago to see the specialist again. The medicine wasn't helping and the specialist said there was little he could do for him. His kidneys were diseased and failing and his liver was also causing problems.

"I'm dying?" Luke asked.

"Yes," the doctor said. "I can give you something to help with the discomfort and pain . . . but . . . "

"How long do I have?"

"Possibly six months," the specialist said. "It's hard to say."

Luke and Hettie returned to Fort Worth and he felt better for awhile, and reopened his card games, but soon was back in bed.

His brother, Joe, came to see him and was shocked at his appearance. He brought word that if Luke would come to San Angelo, their mother would care for him.

Luke shook his head; it was never his way to live with someone else, to impose on them, even his own family. Hettie was taking care of him fine, he told Joe, and he would be happier in his own home.

Shortly thereafter, his brothers, Young and Henry, came to see Luke. They stayed for several days, and Luke thoroughly enjoyed their visit. They relived their early days on the Ouachita River in Arkansas, the family's move to Texas in late 1859, of fighting the raiding Kiowas and Comanche Indians, of old Grandpap Short with his English accent crying, "Avast, yon grand rascals!" to the Indians.

Young had been particularly close with Luke and now he

233

entertained him with stories and jokes and kept him laughing all the time he was there.

In their serious moments, Luke asked Young and Henry to come and assist Hettie when he died. He told them he had bought a burial plot, and his headstone was also paid for. All they had to do was have the date of his death carved on it.

Luke had never been one to say much of the years away from his family, but now, on his good days, he told his brothers of his experiences in Ogallala, Sidney and Camp Robinson, Nebraska. He talked of the trading post he and T. J. had operated near the Red Cloud and Spotted Tail Agencies, of the Indian uprising of 1876 and 1878 when he'd carried dispatches and scouted for Major Thornburgh. He spoke of his time in Denver, Leadville, Deadwood, and Cheyenne, of Tombstone and the Dodge City difficulties with Webster and Deger. He also told them of his shoot out with Jim Courtright, and what had led up to it.

After his two brothers left, Luke was satisfied that his mother and wife would be well taken care of. Perhaps this knowledge lifted his spirits, for within a few days the swelling in his lower body decreased, and he was out of bed.

"Let's go to Chicago and see the Exhibition!" He told Hettie, and they packed their bags and were driven to the train station.

CHAPTER TWENTY-FOUR

Luke enjoyed the World's Columbian Exposition in Chicago. There were hundreds of exhibits to see, among the many that Luke and Hettie observed was the prototype of Karl Benz's four wheeled, mechanical engine powered buggy. They admired the Exposition's classic architecture, and also saw Little Egypt perform her scandalous gyrations on the Midway.

One day Luke and Hettie took a hack to a lot between Sixty-second and Sixty-third Street and attended Buffalo Bill's Wild West show. Luke thoroughly enjoyed it, telling Hettie that despite the lack of space, Bill Cody had shown much of what the Old West had been like. There were real Indians performing, some of whom might have been his adversaries back in the uprisings of 1876-1878. Luke must have had mixed feelings that day, knowing that there were virtually no wild buffalo left in the United States; some said that Buffalo Bill's stage herd was among the largest groups in captivity. Surely Luke must have likened the passing of the buffalo to the passing of the gambler. Perhaps, like many another, he wondered what the future would bring after he was gone.

The World's Columbian Exposition was a huge success, undoubtedly the greatest the country had ever seen. When it was over, some 27,000,000 people had come to see it.

By this time Luke was completely beaten, and Hettie bought a hardwood wheelchair, and pushed him around. The next day Luke told Hettie he had seen enough and wanted to go home. They were on the southbound train the following day.

In Fort Worth, Nat Kramer stopped by to visit with Luke and told him how a sick friend of his had been much relieved by taking baths at a hot springs spa. Luke and Hettie had spent a lot of time at the Gilbert House in Geuda Springs, Kansas, off and on, and knew the manager, S. L. Ward, well. Luke knew he couldn't live long, and decided that the hot springs would be as good a place to die as any. Shortly thereafter he wired Ward reserving his largest private suite.

Luke had always been especially close to his brother, Young. Now he wired Young in Kiowa, Kansas, and asked him to come to Fort Worth. Young was shocked when he saw Luke. His kidneys were failing and his body and face were bloated and grey. Luke told Young he and Hettie wanted to go to Gueda Springs. Young and Hettie packed their things and they boarded the train to Kansas. On their arrival they were met by Mr. Ward with a hack and driven to the Gilbert House.

The Gilbert House was a three story brick building with around fifty rooms and a few suites. Health seekers came to bathe and drink the waters which gushed from seven different springs. Each spring had different properties that were heralded as the cures for everything from hemorrhoids to cancer. Indeed, the waters were bottled and shipped all over the country to be consumed by enthusiastic customers who claimed to have been cured of various illnesses.

Luke didn't believe all the testimonials, but he was a sick man, and the hot mineral baths began to relax him and relieve his discomfort and pains. Soon he was feeling better and his naturally optimistic spirit rebounded.

Geuda Springs had about six hundred permanent residents, several other spas and hotels, a drugstore, groceries, a bank and so forth. It was served by a branch of the Santa Fe Railroad. The Gilbert House did have a telephone and Luke, as his health seemed to improve, began placing bets with various bookmakers and gamblers around the country. He bet on horse races, dog races and prize fights, anything to pass the time and relieve his misery.

Mr. Ward's son, who went by the initials, M. C., was a boy of twelve that summer in 1893, when Luke and Hettie stayed at the Gilbert House. M. C. had heard all the stories of Luke's life, his big no-limit gambling games, and his gunfights. He spent a lot of time in Luke and Hettie's suite, which was one whole wing of the ground floor. The suite had its own huge spa, a small kitchen, two bedrooms and a living room. Luke was still the generous tipper of old, and the boy ran errands around town for medicines at the drug store, groceries, or to place a bet for Luke on the house telephone. M. C. Ward remembered the great gambler and his petite, beautiful wife with the sad eyes some sixty-six years later: "While able to eat in when he first came, he was much wasted by his illness, and soon took to his bed . . . "[1]

1893 was an interesting year in several respects: Hawaii was proclaimed a republic, and annexed by treaty to the United States in February. Herman Goering, the Nazi leader, and Cole Porter, the American songwriter were both born. Henry Ford built his first car, and W. T. Stead lectured on "If Christ came to Chicago." Oscar Wilde, whom Luke had seen at Horace Tabor's opera house in Leadville with his long hair and silken knee breeches, came out with his *A Woman of No Importance*. Fridtjof Nansen began his expedition to the North Pole which was to last for three years and was in the end unsuccessful.

Grover Cleveland had, from the first, been allied with eastern money against the western mining interests. He wanted to abolish the Sherman Silver Puchase Act of 1890 that guaranteed the U. S. Treasury would purchase 4,500,000 ounces of silver a month. After a spirited rise in 1890, the price of silver inched downward. Of further concern for the western silver producers after Cleveland's presidential win in 1892, India, one of the world's largest silver buyers, suddenly ceased coining silver and the metal plunged from a high in 1879 of one dollar and twenty-nine cents an ounce, to sixty-two cents after Cleveland's election. When Cleveland persuaded Congress to scrap the Sherman Act in 1893, silver plunged to fifty cents, and the nation went into a terrible recession, much like the one back in 1873 after Jay Cooke had gone bankrupt and the stock market crashed. Many silver mines in the west closed and never reopened. Multi-millionaires such as Horace Tabor, were paupers overnight when the banks were forced to foreclose.

In September, Luke Short's kidneys failed and there was nothing his doctor in Gueda Springs could do to save him. It was just as well, for he hated being an invalid. The body of this indomitable man was no match for his spirit, and he died in his bed at the Gilbert House.

His life had spanned an incredible era. He had seen the coming of the railroads that spanned the west, and opened up millions of square miles to settlement. He had seen the prairies covered with buffalo, and helped with their demise. He had also helped bring the speckled Texas longhorns to the lush grasslands of Kansas and Nebraska to replace the buffalo, and had lived to see the prairie turned into wheat fields that would become America's bread basket. He had fought Comanches, Kiowas, Sioux and Cheyenne, and lived to see the Indians on reservations and the plains safe for settlers.

He had worked as cowboy, buffalo hide-hunter, army dispatch rider and scout, and finally as one of the most respected high rolling gamblers of his time during what would come to be known as the Golden Age of Gambling.

The legendary generosity of the frontier gambler was exemplified by Luke Short. When he died there were more than $150,000 in loans in his book. He was particularly generous with members of his profession who were down on their luck, or needed backing. Nothing gave him more pleasure than to help an old friend. He had given thousands of dollars to church groups over the years to help build churches, and to take care of orphans, and other good works, though he was himself an agnostic. Like Doc Holliday, whose last words were reported to have been: "This is funny!" Luke might well have said the same, for it was the church groups, to whom he had so generously given, that sounded the knell of death for the profession he had followed.

Legal gambling was all but over. There would be games in isolated places in the west, and in Alaska during the Gold Rush of 1898, but it was really all over except for the shouting. Arizona's old-timers lamented the passing of an era in 1907, when gambling was outlawed. "The Tiger is dying!" announced the *Prescott Journal-Miner*. "He will not be forgotten, nor maligned," said the *Tombstone Prospector*, in referring to the honest gamblers of old. New Mexico followed with stringent anti-gambling laws the following year. Nevada would follow suit in 1910, and it would all be over.

Luke Short did not know about this, of course, for he died there in Gueda Springs, Kansas on September 8, 1893. He had lived an extremely full life, though he was only 39 years of age.

He died without leaving any children, but there would be new Lukes named for him in the Short family. Despite his faults, he had gone his own independent way, never apologizing for his past, nor censoring others.

Hettie had wired two of Luke's brothers, Henry in San Angelo, and Young in Kansas, the day before Luke died. Both men had been keeping up with his state of health, and they immediately got onto trains and headed for Gueda Springs. Luke died just before they arrived. The two brothers and Hettie undressed Luke and washed his body before the undertaker arrived to prepare it for the trip back to Fort Worth.

Young M. C. Ward viewed Luke's body as it was bathed, and saw many old wound scars.[2]

The two brothers and Hettie accompanied Luke's body back to Fort Worth for burial. The services were attended by Hettie, Henry and Young Short, Nat Kramer, and many of his old friends and customers in Fort Worth. It was a quiet affair, nothing like Jim Courtright's grand send off.

Luke Short lies in Fort Worth's Oakwood Cemetery, not far from where Jim Courtright is buried. Sometime later, Courtright's family put up a grand headstone. The inscription reads:

Jim "Longhaired" Courtright

1845-1887

U. S. Army Scout, U. S. Marshal, Frontiersman, Pioneer, Representative of a class of men now passing from Texas who whatever their faults were type of that brave courageous manhood which commands respect and admiration

Luke's plot measures twelve by twenty-four feet in the Oakwood Cemetery on Grand Avenue and Gould Street. At the head of the grave is a simple granite stone stating:

Luke L. Short 1854-1893

Chapter 1

1 Even in the family there has been some disagreement on where Wash and Hettie Short's children were born, and in what order. The author has used the 1860 Montague County, Texas census. It showed in August of that year, Martha, the oldest, was 12 years of age: John, 11; Joe, 10; Young, 8; Luke,6; Mary, 4; and Henry, 2. It also states that all the seven children were born in Arkansas.

The three other children, Bell Nannie, George, and Will, were born in Cooke County, Texas in the mid-1860's.

Chapter 2

1 From Florence Short Self's article in *Old West* magazine, summer edition, 1976, *Luke Short's Brother, Joe.*
    Another account is in a recent *True West* magazine, *Recollections of the Box Family Tragedy*, 1996

Chapter 7

1 *Life of Billy Dixon*, by Olive K. Dixon

2 Bat Masterson's *Human Life series*, Luke Short, April, 1907. (Masterson's dates were wrong. Luke resumed his education as soon as he could afford to buy books.)

3 *Life of Billy Dixon*, by Olive K. Dixon

Chapter 8

1 Much of the background of this chapter is from these sources: *Killing Custer* by James Welch, *Crazy Horse and Custer* by Stephen E. Ambrose, *On the Border with Crook,* by John G. Bourke

Chapter 9

1 *Frontier Times* published a story in the October 1923 issue which said in part: "Luke Short killed five Indians in 1876 in the Black Hills country of South Dakota who attacked him while he was carrying dispatches for General Crook."

The *Rocky Mountaineer*, May 5, 1957, came out with virtually the same story.

In 1900, Carrie DeVoe, wrote of this same incident, naming Luke Short as a government scout.

Chapter 11

1 Bat Masterson, in his 1907 *Human Life* article, told that Luke killed six Indians in Nebraska at this time. The story handed down to the author, was that two of these men were white bootleggers, competitors of his, and were killed the following year.

Chapter 12

Chapter 13

1 U. S. Government report of persons and articles employed and hired at Sidney Barracks, October 1878. Item #8, refers to "Luke Short B5." His services, carrying dispatches from Ogallala to Major Thornburgh, 4th Inf.

 On the 9th of October he was designated as a scout, a "B6" at $100 per month.

Chapter 14

1 See note #1, on Chapter Eleven. Author's father said these two men where white competitors.

2 Luke Short's escape from the train was told by Bat Masterson in his *Human Life* article. It varies little from the story my father told me.

Chapter 15

1 There is no official record of Luke Short's arrest or of his escape from the train. Very likely the Army was embarrassed and didn't report it to the newspapers.

Owen P Whites, in *My Texas 'Tis Of Thee,* said that   Luke Short arrived in Denver with $60,000 from his share of their "whiskey trading" venture.

My own father said this amount was a combination of the whiskey venture, plus the money Luke had saved from buffalo hunting and gambling. There is no doubt that this was a substantial stake in the late 1870's.

Chapter 16

1 Much of the background of Leadville comes from the excellent book by Phyllis Flanders Dorset, *Colorado's Gold and Silver Rushes.*

2 This story keeps coming up, sometimes Luke Short is a player, sometimes the dealer. My understanding is that he was the house dealer when he shot Brown.

3 Luke told his brother, Henry, this story not long before he died.

Chapter 17

1 Much of this chapter's background comes from John Meyers Meyers, *The Last Chance.*

2 *Knights of the Green Cloth,* by Robert K. DeArment

3 Ibid

4 Bat Masterson in, *Human Life*

5 Bat Masterson had a habit of truly picking some of the "damnedest" people for friends. Later, in Denver, he became

friendly with the infamous Randolph "Soapy" Smith, one of the crookedest gamblers who can be imagined. Soapy was the head of a gang of con-men, thieves, and murderers, that later went to Skagway, Alaska during the Gold Rush and drugged and robbed miners in his saloon and out on the trails. He was known as "The King of Thieves" in Skagway. Smith was finally challenged by a member of the Vigilantes, Frank Reid. The two men shot it out, and both men died.

6 Bat Masterson might have killed Corporal King at Sweetwater, Texas, but this was never clear, since several other shots were fired in the altercation between the soldiers and the buffalo hunters. If Masterson did kill King, it was his only killing, despite all the hype.

7 *Knights of the Green Cloth,* Robert K. DeArment

Chapter 18

1 *Knights of the Green Cloth,* Robert K. DeArment

2 *On The Border With Crook,* John G. Bourke

3 Walter L. Short

4 *Dodge City*, Fredric R. Young

Chapter 19

1 Much of this chapter is from:

Dodge City, by Frederic C. Young

Dodge City, Queen of Cowtowns, Stanley Vestal

Great Gunfighters of the Kansas Cowtowns, 1867-1886
Miller and Snell

Wyatt Earp-Frontier Marshal, Stuart N. Lake

Bat Masterson-The Man and the Legend,
Robert K. DeArment

Chapter 21

1 The city of Dodge City, Mayor Deger, and City Marshal, Hinkle, later settled this suit out of court for $8,000.

2 From *Luke Short and His Era,* William R. Cox

3 Walter L. Short

4 Ibid

5 *Bat Masterson,* Robert K. DeArment

6 *Triggernometry,* Eugene Cunningham

7 Jake Johnson's Deposition

8 *Triggernometry,* Eugene Cunningham

Chapter 22

1 *Colorado's Gold and Silver Rushes,* Phyllis Flanders Dorset

Chapter 24

1 From, *Luke Short and His Era,* William R. Cox (Letter to William R. Cox)

2 Ibid

BIBLIOGRAPHY

Ambrose, Stephen E. *Crazy Horse and Custer,*
        Doubleday 1975

Bailey, Lynn R. *A Tenderfoot in Tombstone,*
        Westernlore Press 1995

Bartholomew, Ed *The Biographical Album of Western*
        Gunfighters,
        Houston: Frontier press of Texas 1958

Bourke, James G. *On the Border with Crook,*
        Bison Books 1971

Bruner, Robert K. *A Treasury of Gambling Stories,*
        Chicago: Ziff-Davis, 1946

Burns, Walter Noble *Tombstone,*
        Doubleday 1927-1929

Chaput, Don *The Earp Papers,*
        Affiliated Writers of America 1994

Cox, William R. *Luke Short and His Era,*
        Doubleday 1961

DeArment, Robert K. *Bat Masterson,*
        University of Oklahoma 1979

DeArment, Robert K. *Knights of the Green Cloth,*
University of Oklahoma   1982

Devol, George H. *Forty Years a Gambler on the Mississippi,*
New York: 1892

Dick, Everett *Vanguards of the Frontier,*
Bison Books 1965

Dixon, Olive K. *Life of Billy Dixon,*
State House Press 1987

Dorset, Phyllis F. *Colorado's Gold and Silver Rushes,*
Barnes and Noble 1970

Drago, Harry Sinclair *Great American Cattle Trails,*
Bramhall House 1965

Dykstra, Robert R. *The Cattle Towns,*
Bison Books 1968

Holbrook, Stewart H. *Little Annie Oakley and Other Rugged People,*
MacMillian 1948

Knight, Oliver *Fort Worth: Outpost on the Trinity,*
University of Oklahoma Press 1953

Martin, Charles L. *A Sketch of Sam Bass, the Bandit,*
University of Oklahoma Press 1956

Otero, Miguel A. *My Life on the Frontier,*
Harper Bros, 1927

Quinn, John Philip *Fools of Fortune, or, Gambling and Gamblers,*
G. L. Howe and Co., 1890

Robertson, Frank C., and Beth Kay Harris
Soapy Smith: King of the Frontier Con Men,
HastingHouse,1961

Lee, Wayne C. *Wild Towns of Nebraska,*
Caxton Printers 1992

Miller and Snell *Great Gunfighters of the Kansas Cowtowns,*
University of Nebraska Press 1963

Lake, Stuart N. *Wyatt Earp: Frontier Marshal,*
Houghton Mifflin 1931

Meyers, John Meyers, *Doc Holliday,*
Little, Brown & Co. 1955

------ *The Last Chance,*
E.P. Dutton 1950

Rosa, Joseph G. *Age of the Gunfighter,*
University of Oklahoma Press 1995

Sandoz, Mari *The Buffalo Hunters,*

Bison Books 1954

------   *The Cattlemen,*
           Bison Books 1958

Readers Digest *The Great American West*

Time-Life Book   *The Wild West*

--------------   *The Railroaders*

--------------   *The Cowboys*

--------------   *The Ranchers*

--------------   *The Great Chiefs*

--------------   *The Indians*

--------------   *The Gamblers*

Welch, James *Killing Custer,*
          W. W. Norton 1994

White, Owen P. *My Texas 'Tis of Thee,*
        Books For Libraries Press 1971

Wright, Robert M. *Dodge City: The Cowboy Capitol
and the Great Southwest,*
        Wichita Eagle Press, 1913

Young, Fredric R. *Dodge City,*
High Plains Publishers 1985

Here is what the reviewers said about Wayne Short's Alaskan books:

On *The Cheechakoes:*

"How refreshing it is in this age of the soft American, the Organizational Man in his asphalt jungle of conformity to see that the pioneer spirit still survives, that a man by his own efforts can thrive in the wilderness and hold the basic necessities of life in his hands knowing that he is equal to the challenge before him. This is the heritage of our forefathers, and this is what makes *"The Cheechakoes"* such interesting reading."

Marylin Leathers
The Arizona Republic

This Raw Land

"Wayne Short is an Alaskan commercial fisherman and also a writer and story teller of great talent, as proved by his first book, *"The Cheechakoes,"* and demonstrated again in *"This Raw Land"* originally published by Random House.

Short, who skippers a commercial boat during the fishing season and writes when the snow closes in on the mountains tells a fascinating tale of a life little known in metropolitan Anchorage.

The book is quick reading from start to finish, and evening haunted by the lonely cry of a loon, of humor and danger in an isolated life that is part of the Alaskan heritage.

William J. Tobin
Anchorage DailyTimes

Albie, and Billy, the Sky-Pilot, and Other Stories

"Wayne Short, the man that gave us those great books, *"This Raw Land"* and *"The Cheechakoes"*, is back with a collection of twenty-one true stories. These stories are about local characters that lived around these parts thirty and forty years ago.

Once you've started this book-it is a hard one to put down."

Bob DeArmond
Sitka Daily Sentinel